SHY GIRL

The Story of Eleanor Roosevelt
First Lady of the World

BONNIE
PONY OF THE SIOUX
THE JUNGLE SECRET
NORTH POLE: THE STORY OF
  ROBERT PEARY
BASEBALL BONUS KID
CAROL HEISS: OLYMPIC QUEEN
GREEN LIGHT FOR SANDY
SEA TREASURE
THE BLOOD RED BELT
KENDALL OF THE COAST GUARD
RODEO ROUNDUP
NANCY KIMBALL, NURSE'S AIDE
FOOTBALL FURY
CIVIL WAR SAILOR
DINNY AND DREAMDUST
AUSTIN OF THE AIR FORCE
THE LONG REACH
FOOTLIGHTS FOR JEAN
BASEBALL SPARK PLUG
RUNAWAY TEEN
LIGHTNING ON ICE
HOT ROD THUNDER
JUDY NORTH, DRUM MAJORETTE
DIRT TRACK DANGER
ADVENTURE IN ALASKA
CLIMB TO THE TOP
FISHING FLEET BOY
JACK WADE, FIGHTER FOR
  LIBERTY
THE MYSTERY OF HIDDEN
  HARBOR
SCANLON OF THE SUB SERVICE
A SUMMER TO REMEMBER
NAT DUNLAP, JUNIOR "MEDIC"
BLAST-OFF! A TEEN ROCKET
  ADVENTURE
TWO GIRLS IN NEW YORK
THE MYSTERY OF THE FLOODED
  MINE
CATHY AND LISETTE
EVANS OF THE ARMY
HIGH SCHOOL DROP OUT
DOUBLE TROUBLE
PRO FOOTBALL ROOKIE
THE MYSTERY OF BLUE STAR
  LODGE

ADVENTURE IN DEEPMORE CAVE
FAST BALL PITCHER
HI PACKETT, JUMPING CENTER
NURSE IN TRAINING
SHY GIRL: THE STORY OF
  ELEANOR ROOSEVELT
SKI PATROL
BIG BAND
GINNY HARRIS ON STAGE
GRACIE
THREE CHEERS FOR POLLY
SECOND YEAR NURSE
FEAR RIDES HIGH
THE MYSTERY OF THE INSIDE
  ROOM
ARTHUR ASHE: TENNIS CHAMPION
THE MYSTERY OF THE
  THIRD-HAND SHOP
GOING, GOING, GONE
THE KID FROM CUBA: ZOILO
  VERSALLES
GANG GIRL
TV DANCER
ROAR OF ENGINES
DONNA DEVARONA: GOLD MEDAL
  SWIMMER
PETE CASS: SCRAMBLER
BLACK SOLDIER
QUEEN OF ENGLAND: THE STORY
  OF ELIZABETH I
TROUBLE AT MERCY HOSPITAL
TRAPPED IN SPACE
MARTIN LUTHER KING: FIGHTER
  FOR FREEDOM
DANCE! THE STORY OF
  KATHERINE DUNHAM
THE TOMMY DAVIS STORY
FIRST LADY OF INDIA: THE
  STORY OF INDIRA GANDHI
RUNAWAY
SHIRLEY CHISHOLM
THREE WHO DARED
I WAS A BLACK PANTHER
THE TRUTH ABOUT DRUGS
MIGHTY HARD ROAD

SHY GIRL

The Story of Eleanor Roosevelt
First Lady of the World

BY MIRIAM GILBERT

Illustrated by
Herbert McClure

Doubleday & Company, Inc.
Garden City, New York

Library of Congress Catalog Card Number 65-14021

Copyright © 1965 by Doubleday & Company, Inc.

All Rights Reserved

Printed in the United States of America

Prepared by ℬ Rutledge Books

ABOUT THIS BOOK . . .

Eleanor Roosevelt was an ugly duckling who became the world's most loved woman.

Her story can be found in part in newspaper headlines, in part in her autobiography, in part in letters, in part in books, in part in official records.

The facts of her childhood are known. Her feelings are revealed in what she wrote about herself. Her inner thoughts and many words spoken in intimate conversation can only be conjectured.

Shy Girl: The Story of Eleanor Roosevelt, First Lady of the World, is written about real people and real happenings. It tells its story using words and thoughts as true as the truth is known to the author and editors.

To Holle,
Andrea's best friend—
whose courage, in her own small way,
in her own brief life, was as great
as that of Eleanor Roosevelt

Contents

SHY GIRL

The Story of Eleanor Roosevelt
First Lady of the World

CHAPTER 1

Always a Disgrace

"Sit still!" Madeleine snapped at Eleanor. She pulled the brush roughly through the girl's long brown hair. "Don't you want to look nice for your first day of lessons?" she asked.

Seven-year-old Eleanor Roosevelt shivered. She had always been afraid of Madeleine, the family's French maid. Secretly, Eleanor was afraid of many things—including these new lessons she was going to take. But in the Roosevelt family, no one ever admitted that he was afraid of anything.

Eleanor stood up as Madeleine tied a blue bow in her hair. The maid stood back to examine the tall, thin girl. "That's the best I can do," she said with a sigh. "Your mother is waiting to see you before you go to the class room. Don't you keep her waiting any longer," she said.

Eleanor hurried to her mother's room. Mrs. Roosevelt was lying on the bed, her light brown hair framing her face. "My mother is the most beautiful woman in the world," Eleanor thought, as she walked quietly into the room.

Slowly, Mrs. Roosevelt opened her eyes. "I've been expecting you," she said, sitting up. She held Eleanor at arm's length, examining her daughter's pale, narrow face, her long, thin arms and legs.

"I buy the finest clothes for you," her mother said, shaking her head, "but they never look right."

Eleanor knew that she was not a pretty girl. What hurt most about not being pretty was how disappointed her mother was in her. Mrs. Roosevelt was a famous beauty from a family of beauties. Even Eleanor's grandmother was lovely to look at, a woman of grace and charm. How dreadful it was to have an ugly duckling in this well-known family.

Eleanor was well aware of how important looks seemed to be to a family as famous as the Roosevelts. It would have been so wonderful to be like the other handsome members of the family.

Eleanor lived with her mother and her two younger brothers in a very large brown stone house on East 61st Street, one of the very "best" sections of New York City. Her brother Elliott, Jr., was three, and Hall was not quite a year old.

It was a home without a father. Eleanor could not understand why her beloved parent was almost never with them any more. Post cards would come to her and she would read his messages of love, and on birthdays and Christmas there would be beautiful presents. But she rarely saw him.

The house was carefully run by the servants. Eleanor's mother was out more than she was in. Mornings meant going to New York's fine stores. Afternoons were for calling on friends in her carriage, with a coach man to drive the horses. At least one day a week, Mrs. Roosevelt entertained in the handsome drawing room. The guest list was filled with the names of prominent people.

Evenings were taken up with dinner parties and fancy dress balls. Also, there were the theater and the opera to attend. New York in the year 1891 was the center of culture in the United States. Stars from all over the world came to the city to perform.

And no matter where beautiful Anna Hall Roosevelt went, she was the center of attention.

In those days, most children of such wealthy families had private teachers instead of attending regular schools. Mrs. Roosevelt had set up a class room on the top floor of the house just for Eleanor, and had hired a Miss Tomes, who had a fine reputation as a teacher.

Now the morning had arrived when Eleanor was to have her first lessons.

Eleanor stood waiting for her mother to say something

more. Mrs. Roosevelt put her hand to her forehead. Eleanor bent over her. "Do you have a headache, Mama?" she asked. "May I rub your head for you, the way you like me to sometimes?"

"Just for a few moments," her mother agreed, resting back on the pillows. "I don't want you to keep your new teacher waiting."

Gently, lightly, Eleanor rubbed the smooth white forehead. As her hands glided back and forth, she felt very close to her mother. If only she dared tell her how she felt! But revealing her feelings was another thing Eleanor was afraid to do.

"Thank you. That will be enough," her mother said. "Now, before you go, I want to review some spelling words with you."

Mrs. Roosevelt stood up and slipped into a pale pink silk robe. At the sight of it, Eleanor had a sudden lonely feeling. "That was the robe that Papa gave her," she thought. How much she loved her father—and how much she missed him!

Her father had bought the robe when they were all in Paris, the summer before. Mr. and Mrs. Roosevelt, Eleanor and her little brother Elliott had been in Europe, traveling, for several months. Soon there would be a new baby and the family settled down near Paris to await its arrival.

A few weeks later they had sailed for home—all but Mr. Roosevelt. Eleanor's father stayed behind in Paris.

He was ill, Eleanor was told, and he could not travel.

Some time later, when he returned to the United States, Eleanor's father went down to Virginia, to a farm. "To rest some more," Eleanor heard. Now, almost a year later, he was still there.

When, Eleanor wondered, would her father come back to them? He was so gay, so much fun. Life was so different when he was home. She was always happy when she could be with him.

"Stop day dreaming, child!" Eleanor's mother said sharply. "Now sit down. I want to go over your spelling with you."

The words were easy enough. Eleanor spelled them all correctly, as her mother read them off to her.

"All right," Mrs. Roosevelt said, when they were finished, "run upstairs. Tell Miss Tomes I will come up later to see how everything is going."

Now that the moment had come, Eleanor could hardly drag her feet up the thickly carpeted stairs to the third floor. She was so afraid of new people! She dreaded what they would think when they saw the plain, clumsy daughter of beautiful Anna Hall Roosevelt.

"I shall be a disgrace to my mother," Eleanor thought sadly.

If only her father were here! He wouldn't send her off by herself. He would understand that she was afraid. Her father knew her better than anyone else. He knew just what to do to make her feel brave. He would have called her "Little Nell," his pet name for her, and taken her by the hand and brought her up to the new teacher himself . . .

"Eleanor, you are going to be late!" her mother called.

Eleanor hurried along. At last, she reached the new class room.

She stood outside the door, feeling as if she couldn't breathe. Miss Tomes, the teacher, motioned to her. "Come in, Eleanor. Here is your chair."

Eleanor stumbled to her seat, staring at the teacher. Miss Tomes opened a book.

"We will start with a few simple spelling words." The teacher smiled. "Spell *brother*, Eleanor."

Eleanor opened her mouth, but no sound came out. It was as if a blackboard eraser had been wiped across her mind.

"It's not a hard word," Miss Tomes urged. "*Brother* —like *mother*."

"Yes," Eleanor thought in confusion, "my brothers are like my mother. They are dear, pretty boys. Everyone fusses over them, and . . ."

"Surely you can spell *brother*," Miss Tomes said gently. "What letter does it begin with?"

There was a rustle of silk from the doorway. Then her mother's voice said sharply, "Eleanor, spell *brother!* You spelled it for me not half an hour ago!"

Looking up, Eleanor saw that her mother's face was flushed with shame.

Mrs. Roosevelt gazed past her at the teacher. "Please excuse my daughter," she said in a strained voice. She seized Eleanor by the hand and pulled her down the stairs to her room.

"Why must you always disgrace me?" she cried, when they were alone. "You are not a stupid child—why do you behave as if you were?"

Eleanor's lips trembled. "I was afraid . . ."

"Afraid!" Mrs. Roosevelt echoed in surprise. "Afraid in your own house? Afraid of what?"

Eleanor reached out her hand. "Mama—" she began.

"I don't know what I am going to do with you!" her mother cried. She turned and left the room, beautiful even in her anger.

Seven-year-old Eleanor dug her fingernails into her palms, gulping back the hot tears that filled her eyes. She was ugly. She was stupid. She was not good for anything. She was a failure—all her life long she would be a failure!

CHAPTER 2

A Liar

As the weeks passed, and the new teacher and class room seemed less strange, Eleanor began to feel more comfortable. She had a remarkable memory and Miss Tomes was pleased with her progress. School work became a pleasant way to fill the lonely hours.

One afternoon, while Eleanor was up in her room doing her lessons, she heard the sound of voices in the drawing room. Curious, she went downstairs, walked quietly to the open door of the drawing room and looked in. Her aunt was sitting on the sofa next to her mother. Her cousin Alice, the same age as Eleanor, was curled up in an armchair, looking at the pictures of fashions in the magazine *Harper's Weekly*.

Eleanor started forward. Then she stopped. She was

not allowed to enter the drawing room unless her mother gave her permission. How she would love to walk directly in and throw herself into her aunt's arms! Eleanor loved her aunt. She was her father's oldest sister—and that made her special, to begin with. Besides, anyone who was in trouble or needed help always turned to her. The family called her Auntie Bye.

Eleanor waited patiently for someone to notice her. She stared at her pretty blue-eyed cousin Alice, who looked like a doll sitting there in the chair.

Auntie Bye had taken care of Alice when her mother had died, two days after Alice was born. Alice's father, Theodore Roosevelt, had married again two years later, but Alice still came to visit Auntie Bye quite often.

The maid was passing around a tray of candies and sweet pastries. Eleanor's mouth watered. She dared to take a step forward.

Her mother glanced up. "Come in, Granny." She motioned to Eleanor. "You look as serious as an old lady!"

Eleanor felt herself blush. She hung her head as she greeted her aunt. "Good afternoon, Auntie Bye," she muttered.

"Well, go along, say hello to your cousin Alice," her mother told her.

The maid was standing in front of Alice with the tray of sweets. Eleanor was staring so hard at the candies that she didn't notice the curved leg of the chair. She tripped and almost knocked the tray from the maid's hand.

Eleanor knew from the look on her mother's face that she could not have any of the candy. Eleanor loved sweets, but her mother would seldom allow her to have cake or candy. Now that she had been so clumsy, her mother would surely say no!

Alice popped a piece of chocolate in her mouth and smacked her lips. Eleanor turned to her mother. "Just one piece?" she begged.

Her mother shook her head firmly.

"I'm spending a few days with Auntie Bye," Alice said. She stood up like a grand lady and smoothed the wrinkles from her dress. "We would like you to come to play tomorrow afternoon. We can have a tea party."

Eleanor gazed silently at Alice. How pretty she looked. How easily she spoke! She didn't have to hunt and struggle for words. If she could just be like her cousin.

All of the Roosevelts seemed to have a magic gift for speaking well. Alice's father, Theodore, was in Washington, D.C., making quite a stir with his speeches.

"Eleanor!" Her mother's voice cut into her wandering thoughts. "Why don't you take Alice upstairs and show her some of your school work?"

"I hear that you are doing quite well." Auntie Bye smiled.

Eleanor's blue eyes lit up. "I hope so," she said. "As soon as I can I want to write my father long letters."

Eleanor's mother laughed lightly, interrupting her. "The child is wild about her father." She turned to the girls. "Now run along, both of you. We will call you when Auntie Bye is ready to leave."

As Eleanor started up the long flight of stairs, she spied the cook going down to the basement store room where the grocery supplies were kept. Eleanor turned around and ran into the kitchen, Alice following her.

"What are you doing?" Alice asked.

"I'm looking for something. Please be quiet," Eleanor whispered.

Eleanor opened the door of the pantry closet. Sure enough, there on the very first shelf were two opened bags of candy. Eleanor took one bag. She passed the other to Alice.

Suddenly, there came the sound of steps in the long hall way leading to the kitchen. Frightened, Eleanor took the bag of candy and stuffed it down the front of her dress.

Madeleine, the French maid, came in and looked around. "What are you doing?" Madeleine demanded. "Where is cook?"

"She is downstairs," Eleanor said, backing slowly out of the door. Alice quietly slipped away, down the hall.

"What are you hiding?" Madeleine asked.

"N-nothing," Eleanor said.

Madeleine spun Eleanor around to face her. The paper bag made a noise under Eleanor's dress.

"What are you hiding?" Madeleine repeated, putting out her hand.

Trembling, Eleanor pulled out the bag, filled with squashed candies. "Please, Madeleine," she begged, "please don't tell Mama!"

Without a word, Madeleine dragged Eleanor into the drawing room. She told Mrs. Roosevelt what Eleanor had done.

"I despise liars!" Her mother stood up, her eyes flashing with anger. "My father taught me never to lie. It's a sin."

Eleanor had been told many times how strict her grandfather had been in raising his children. "I have tried to bring you up properly, the same way," her mother told Eleanor, flinging out her hands in despair. She seized Eleanor by the shoulders. "Go to your room and stay there the rest of the day. And you are to go to bed without supper."

As Eleanor climbed the stairs to her room, the memory of a day in Paris came flooding back.

It had been the summer before, on their travel in Europe. When they stopped in Paris, where Mrs. Roosevelt awaited the birth of Hall, Eleanor was told she was going to be sent to a convent until after the baby was born. Eleanor's father was also going away—to a hospital.

Things turned out worse than usual for Eleanor at the convent. The little French girls kept away from her and did not invite her to join in their games. The time dragged by in dull unhappy days.

Then, one day, one of the girls, by accident, swallowed

a penny. Eleanor watched with envy while the village doctor was summoned and the head of the convent came running. People rushed back and forth, consulting and exclaiming. Eleanor was wide-eyed. How thrilling to have people make such a to-do over you! If only she had been lucky enough to swallow a penny!

Eleanor's blue eyes lighted up. Why not pretend that she had done the same thing? Then everybody would notice her. Off Eleanor raced, crying out, "Teacher, my stomach hurts. I swallowed a penny."

The results were terrible. The teacher didn't believe Eleanor for a moment. She was only annoyed and angry with the trouble Eleanor was causing. Her mother was sent for. Very upset, Mrs. Roosevelt took Eleanor away at once.

Eleanor sat in a corner of the carriage as it pulled away from the convent and bumped along the highway to Paris.

"Why must you make trouble for me now?" Mrs. Roosevelt scolded. "I'm busy looking after your new baby brother—not to speak of your father!"

Eleanor's face shone. "Is Papa home from the hospital?" she asked.

"Yes," her mother answered, "but not for long." Mrs. Roosevelt stared at Eleanor. "I want you to tell your father the truth about what happened at school today," she told her daughter.

Eleanor looked up at her mother. "I lied about the

penny," she admitted, trembling. "I lied because . . ." But she couldn't put the reason into words.

"There is absolutely no reason for lying!" Her mother's face grew dark with anger. "Lying is as bad as stealing," she said.

Eleanor shook herself as if she had wakened from a deep sleep. It was late. The shadows in her room were as black as the night outside her window. Auntie Bye and cousin Alice must have left long ago. How could they have gone without saying good-by to her? Her mother must really be very angry with her. Would her father be angry, too?

Her father wouldn't treat her this way, she thought. Her father loved her, even though she was ugly and scared—and a liar. He hadn't thought that she was so bad when she had confessed lying to him that time in Paris. He hadn't even punished her. He had understood that she was lonely.

Eleanor walked to the window, drawing back the white lace curtains. She gazed up at the sky, where a star flickered feebly, like a dying candle.

"Star light, star bright," she began, "first star I see tonight—" She dropped the curtains and turned back to her dark room. What was the use of wishes? Who said they would come true?

She scratched at her itchy long black stockings. No one cared about her. They had forgotten all about her, up in her room. "I wish I may, I wish I might," she went on, "have the wish, I wish tonight!" Even if wishes never did come true—well, you couldn't tell without trying, could you? Just once something, a miracle, might happen!

She threw herself on the bed and buried her head under the pillows. "I love you, Papa. Come home to me," she cried out to the empty room. "Please come home to me!" she wailed.

CHAPTER 3

"I Don't Know How to Tell You..."

The pattern of Eleanor's life was shattered soon after she became eight years old.

On a cold morning in December, Eleanor was in her room, reading a book. Madeleine came bursting in. "Quickly, quickly!" Madeleine ordered. "Get your coat on at once. You are to go to Mrs. Parish's house."

"To cousin Susie?" Eleanor put down her book. "Why?"

"There's no time to answer questions now," Madeleine snapped. "Do as I say." She fetched Eleanor's coat from the closet and thrust the girl's thin arms into the sleeves. "If you had your nose out of your precious book for a minute, you would know that your mother is sick."

Eleanor looked puzzled. "Sick? What's wrong?"

Madeleine threw her hands up in despair. "You are stupid!" Madeleine pushed Eleanor toward the door. "Hurry along. I have to dress your little brothers, too." She gave a final tug to Eleanor's blue velvet bonnet, setting it straight. "Your grandmother is waiting downstairs to see you before you leave."

"Grandmother Hall is here?"

"Now, with your mother on her death bed, where would you expect your grandmother to be?"

Just then Grandmother Hall came into Eleanor's room. "Hold your tongue, Madeleine," Mrs. Hall said. "Is the child ready?"

"Yes, Ma'am," Madeleine muttered, starting to leave the room.

"Madeleine," Grandmother Hall added, "the arrangements have all been made. Eleanor is to go to Mrs. Parish, as you know. You are to drop the boys off at Mrs. Ludlow's." Mrs. Ludlow was Eleanor's mother's aunt.

It was all a puzzle to Eleanor. Why were she and her brothers being rushed out of the house?

Eleanor went slowly down the stairs. She noticed Bob Ferguson, a young friend of the family, sitting outside of her mother's room. Bob waved to her. Eleanor was surprised to see that his eyes were red from crying. Eleanor waited on the steps as the doctor and a lady in white came out of her mother's room. They whispered together in the hall.

"Eleanor," Madeleine called, "the carriage is waiting."

As she continued down, Eleanor thought, "I will ask cousin Susie what is happening." Mrs. Parish was Eleanor's godmother and had always taken a special interest in her. But when Eleanor arrived at Mrs. Parish's house, even cousin Susie brushed off Eleanor's questions.

Finally, that evening, when Mrs. Parish tucked Eleanor into bed, she explained that Eleanor's mother had diphtheria, a very serious disease. It could easily be caught by others in the same house. The doctor had suggested that the children be sent away.

"Is she going to die?" Eleanor asked, recalling Madeleine's words. "Madeleine said Mother was on her death bed."

"Go to sleep now, Eleanor. We can talk about this at another time."

The time came very soon. It was the evening of December 7th, 1892. It was long past Eleanor's bedtime, but cousin Susie seemed too occupied to notice. Eleanor stood looking out of the window at the horse-drawn carriages passing by. She turned as cousin Susie came to take her to bed. Mrs. Parish did not say anything for a long time. She stayed quietly at Eleanor's side.

"Eleanor," she said, "I don't know how to tell you." She touched the girl's shoulder gently. "Your mother died today."

Eleanor stood in the room, trying to understand the

tragedy of being left without a mother. The flood of tears that cousin Susie must have expected did not come.

Eleanor stared at her godmother, puzzled. Death was entirely strange to her. Even the meaning of the word was not clear in her mind. She stood at the window, turning over the news of her mother's death in her thoughts. The understanding that her beautiful mother was lost forever was sudden.

"You mean I won't see my mother any more?" Eleanor's voice shook.

Cousin Susie nodded, unable to answer. "So young," she murmured, under her breath. She turned away from Eleanor. "Anna was just 29. So young," cousin Susie repeated, "and so beautiful."

Eleanor caught the last words. "My mother was the most beautiful woman in the whole world," she said. "When she dressed up to go to a party, she looked like a queen." Eleanor thought a moment. "And—and—when my father was with her, he looked like a king."

"Your father is coming to New York as fast as he can," cousin Susie said.

Eleanor's heart began to pound. Her father was coming home! Her father would make things right for her. They would be together again, at long last. The tragedy of her mother's death was swept away. . . .

Day by day, Eleanor waited for her father. When he finally came, the meeting was not the joyful one she had expected. Cousin Susie had left them alone in the parlor.

Eleanor felt suddenly shy in front of her father. He was wearing a black suit and his eyes looked heavy and sad. He seemed like a stranger to her.

For a moment they stood still, simply looking at one another. Then, at last, her father put out his hands to her. "Come, Little Nell," he said.

Eleanor rushed into her father's arms. She buried her face against the dark cloth of his suit. She was his "Little Nell" again, his beloved daughter. She felt safe—safe enough to ask, "Papa, when am I going to live with you?"

Mr. Roosevelt turned his head away. "I have been speaking to your Grandmother Hall," he began. His voice was low, and Eleanor had to lean forward to hear him. "The family thinks it best for you and your brothers to live with her." He took Eleanor's cold hand in his and pressed it against him. "Your mother wanted it that way," he added.

"Are you going away again?" Eleanor asked.

"I will write to you. I will visit you often," her father promised. "You must stay closer to me than ever before. You and your brothers are all I have left."

A short while later, Eleanor and her brothers went to live with Grandmother Hall, in a large house at 11 West 37th Street. Madeleine came along to take care of the little boys.

There were many other servants in the house. There were Victor, and Kitty, the maid, with whom Eleanor made fast friends. Eleanor's two young and beautiful aunts, Pussie and Maude, and her two uncles, Vallie and Eddie, also lived there.

Eleanor did her best to please the people around her. She learned that her Aunt Pussie had strange moods. One day she would join Eleanor in a game of hide-and-seek, the next day she would pay no attention to her or scold her for a simple mistake. But Eleanor loved her aunt and learned to accept her moods. Eagerly she ran errands for Pussie and Maude—only too delighted that they paid any attention to her.

Maude was carrying on the family tradition of being a popular young lady. She had many young men calling on her, and Eleanor listened wide-eyed to her talk of gay parties.

In spite of all that went on in her Grandmother Hall's house, there was an empty place in Eleanor's life that only her father could fill.

At last, her father came to visit, as he had promised. Quietly, Eleanor went to meet him in the library. Eleanor had learned not to make noise in Grandmother Hall's house.

She sat down stiffly in a chair, facing her father. Her heart beat with fresh hope. Perhaps he had come to take her and her brothers away, this very day, to live with him.

But once again, there seemed to be other things Mr. Roosevelt wanted to talk about. He told Eleanor he wanted her to study the piano. He enjoyed music very much and he hoped it would bring Eleanor pleasure, too. He encouraged Eleanor to take pride in the way she looked. He urged her to take care of her brothers.

"Elliott and Hall are very young," he said gently. "It is up to you to be a little mother to them." He paused. "Of course, no one—no one in the whole world—can ever take the place of your mother." He seemed unable to go on for a long time.

"I will learn how to keep house for you," Eleanor said, breaking the silence. "Madeleine is teaching me how to sew. I am not very good yet. She gets angry with me and makes me pull out the whole thing if she does not like my stitches. But I am trying."

Her father laughed softly, and it made Eleanor feel good to see a little of her father's usual cheerful manner return. "When I was at cousin Susie's house," Eleanor went on, "I watched her cook and—"

Her father stood up suddenly and went to her side. He crushed her against him. "My Little Nell, a home is where love is. I don't need someone who knows how to cook or someone who knows how to sew. I need someone like you, who will love me as I am."

"I do, Papa—oh, I do!" Eleanor cried out.

"I know," he replied, stroking her long brown hair. "Some day you are going to grow up into a fine young woman. I will proudly point you out to everyone and say, 'That's my daughter, Eleanor'."

The note of sadness had left his voice. He began spinning dreams for Eleanor. Soon they would live together, he assured her.

He told her about his life in Virginia. He described the many horses and dogs he had. He promised to bring Mohawk, his best fox-hunting horse, to New York, and take Eleanor for a ride in Central Park.

His words cast a spell of happiness around Eleanor. There were so many things her father told her, as if he were trying to make up for lost time. When he left, Eleanor sighed with pleasure. Her father had given her a golden future, something worth looking forward to.

CHAPTER 4

Good-by

The dream began to fall apart almost as soon as it had come into being.

In the spring of 1893, Eleanor's brothers, Elliott and Hall, came down with scarlet fever. Eleanor was rushed off to cousin Susie's once more.

One afternoon, her father came to visit her there. He was dressed in black, and Eleanor could see at once that his thoughts were as dark. A shiver went through her. What was it this time? What had happened?

Her father explained. Elliott, already weak from scarlet fever, had caught diphtheria.

"Like Mama?" Eleanor gasped.

"Yes, like Mama. Eleanor, your brother is dead." Mr. Roosevelt added quickly, "Hall is getting better. As soon as he is well, you will be able to go back to live with your grandmother."

Eleanor stood very still. Again, death had little meaning for her. But life—that was something she thought about! She gathered her courage. "Papa—can't we live with you? I could keep house for you. I am learning—"

Her voice trailed away as her father shook his head sadly. "Not yet, Little Nell," he told her. "Not yet . . ."

Once again, life fell into a pattern for Eleanor. Grandmother Hall had fixed habits, and the little girl had to go along with the older woman's way of living.

Grandmother Hall owned two houses. Summers were spent near the village of Tivoli, on the Hudson River, in

a large home in a country-estate area. On exactly the same date every fall, the family returned to the town house in New York City.

Eleanor's grandmother felt that she had been entirely too easy-going with her own children. In Eleanor and Hall she saw an opportunity to correct her mistakes, and she set up a strict schedule and set of rules which the two children must follow.

Eleanor's time was taken up with a busy round of studies. There were her usual classes with private teachers at home. But now there were lessons in social dancing and piano and French. Her grandmother hoped that the social graces she gained through these studies would help Eleanor overcome her clumsy manner and make up for her lack of beauty.

Eleanor worked hard at her studies. She did her best to satisfy her Grandmother Hall's every wish. She didn't complain when she was fitted with a stiff, heavy brace to correct her round shoulders. She couldn't find the courage to explain that she stooped because she was so much taller than other girls—and because the dresses Grandmother considered suitable were so much shorter than other girls'!

Eleanor's life was full—yet it was empty. The only days that seemed to count were those few when her father came to visit.

During the long waits between visits, her father wrote Eleanor letters. They were such wonderful letters! In them he talked to her about all that she was doing and all the things he wanted her to learn.

Eleanor treasured each of her father's letters. She took seriously each word he wrote. Mr. Roosevelt had only to mention a favorite author once and Eleanor would begin to read his books. She kept all of the letters and whenever she was lonely—or frightened—she took them out and read them over again.

Eleanor seemed always to be waiting for the sound of her father's voice. It rang in her ears like no other sound in the world. Sometimes Eleanor would hear him all the way up in her bedroom on the second floor of the 37th Street house. He would hardly be inside the door before Eleanor would come flying down the stairs. Sometimes the stairs weren't fast enough—then she would slide down the stair rail right into her father's arms.

Always she asked the question: "How soon will we be together?" And all too soon her father's visit would be over—and the question left without an answer.

On August 14, 1894, when Eleanor was ten years old, the dream shattered forever.

Her father suffered a fatal heart attack. Aunt Pussie and Aunt Maude broke the news of her father's death to Eleanor.

"I don't believe you," Eleanor cried.

"It's true," Aunt Maude told her gently.

"We know how you feel, Eleanor," Aunt Pussie added.

Now, for the first time, death was a real—and a terrible —thing to the little girl. Death was dreadful truth, bringing an end to all her fond hopes.

"You *don't* know how I feel!" Eleanor sobbed. "No one ever knew how I felt, except Papa." She wiped her eyes with the back of her hands. "I won't believe you! I won't believe you," she screamed.

She stumbled up the stairs to her room. Pulling open the drawer of her desk, she took out the package of her father's letters. "You are alive, Papa, you are alive!"

Eleanor pressed the letters to her face. Tears spilled down her cheeks and she could not stop them.

At last she spread the letters out on the bed. Her eyes burned from the stinging pain of her tears, but she opened each letter and read it over.

Then her eyes fell on a line in her father's last letter. *Good night, my darling little daughter . . .*

Eleanor held the letter tightly. Her thin shoulders shook with fresh grief. Was it *good night* or was it *good-by?* Was her father really dead? Had he really gone from her forever?

CHAPTER 5

A Time for Fun

Eleanor sat down on the dock, spreading the long skirt of her swimming suit neatly around her.

"Jump in," her Uncle Ted urged.

"But I—I don't know how to swim," Eleanor protested.

"Everybody knows how to swim," her uncle replied. "Look," he said and he took three-year-old Ethel and dropped her off the dock. Ethel landed with a splash and began to paddle, bobbing up and down in the water like a cork. Uncle Ted dived in after her.

In a minute, he came out, lifting Ethel up on the dock. The young swimmer ran off to the beach and began to play in the sand. Uncle Ted sat down beside Eleanor.

"Swimming is really very easy," he assured her.

"I'm not very good at sports," Eleanor told him.

"Grandmother Hall doesn't think that sports are lady-like," she added.

"Let me show you," cousin Alice said. She made a clean dive from the dock's edge into the water.

"Here goes!" cousin Kermit called out, running off the end of the dock. He tumbled into the water like a clown, feet first, his hands waving about wildly.

"Try it," Uncle Ted encouraged Eleanor.

Kermit grinned as he came up for air. "All you can do is drown," he said, laughing.

Mr. Roosevelt took Eleanor's hand and led her to the edge of the dock. "Give it a try—just this once," he said.

Eleanor hesitated. The water looked cool and inviting. She couldn't be afraid of everything all her life.

She heard her Uncle Ted counting behind her.

"One, two, three, go!" he roared.

Eleanor jumped. The water was over her head. It filled her nose, her ears. She splashed about wildly, coughing and gasping for breath.

"Move your hands," Uncle Ted shouted to her. "Kick your legs."

It was no use. Eleanor could not move. This was something she would never, *never* be able to do!

Her uncle dived in and immediately pulled her out of the water. "The first time is always the hardest," he said, trying to cheer her. "Next time you will do much better, I assure you."

But there was no next time. As she sat on the beach, watching the others, Eleanor felt sure there would never be a time when she would find the courage to go into the water again.

Waiting for the swim to end, Eleanor sat alone on the dock, looking out across the blue and green water of Long Island Sound.

How she loved it here at Sagamore Hill! Even her swimming failure hadn't dulled the joy of being part of this happy family. She had looked forward so eagerly to the time when Grandmother Hall would allow Eleanor to spend this week in the country with Uncle Ted and his family.

There was Uncle Ted himself, big, red-faced, with his wonderfully large mustache. There were her cousin Alice, the one Eleanor felt closest to, and Ted, Jr., who looked so much like his father. Then there were Kermit and Ethel and the baby, Archie.

There was always something to do, fun to be had, at Sagamore Hill. There were games of hide-and-seek to play in the woods. There were picnics on the beach, walks to take, songs to sing at night around the piano. Eleanor loved especially sitting on the huge front porch of the big, old house high up on the hill, facing out to the Sound. She would sit in her favorite chair, a book to read held comfortably in her lap.

Sometimes she day dreamed. What would it be like to be an Uncle Ted, a man with an important job in the nation's capital? How would it feel to have other people look up to you?

Eleanor had heard from Grandmother Hall that Uncle Ted was fighting against something called the "spoils system." This, Eleanor was told, was a bad practice in the government. After each election for President of the United States, many men working for the government were turned out of their jobs because they didn't belong to the political party that had won the election.

Uncle Theodore called this a national disgrace. He wanted jobs in government to be separated from politics, so that no one could be fired simply because he was a Democrat or a Republican.

Already, here in her first day at Sagamore, Eleanor had heard her uncle talking about the system and how wrong it was.

"Ready for lunch?" her uncle called from the edge of the water.

Eleanor nodded. She *was* hungry. Her Aunt Edith was already coming down the path carrying a large basket covered with a white cloth. Inside, there was sure to be all kinds of wonderful sandwiches and cool drinks and delicious cakes and cookies.

This was one of the things Eleanor loved about coming here. So much of the family fun seemed to happen on the spur of the moment, without planning.

"Game of hide-and-seek?" Ted, Jr., called out as the last crumb of cake disappeared.

With a shout everyone was off for the hay-filled barn. In the dusty dark of the barn, Uncle Ted flopped about, searching for the children hidden in the corners. The straw caught in his bushy mustache and he growled and pretended to be a walrus.

Just as quickly, the game ended and they were running back to the beach to jump into the boat and shove off for a trip around the point.

"Cooper's Bluff," Uncle Ted suggested when the boat trip had ended and they all had joined in dragging the boat safely up on the shore, out of the reach of the highest tide.

Cooper's Bluff was a steep hill which swept down to the water's edge at a sharp angle. As all of them climbed up the hill, Eleanor wondered what new game her uncle might have thought up.

She found out soon enough. She had scarcely caught her breath when her uncle arranged all of the children in a single line, each clasping the other's hand, forming a human chain. Uncle Ted went to the head of the line.

"We are going to see how fast we can get down to the bottom of the hill," he called out—and off they ran.

Eleanor held on for dear life to her cousin Alice's hand as they went racing down the hill, slipping and sliding at a breath-taking pace.

Frightened, Eleanor closed her eyes as they approached

the bottom of the hill and neared the shore. They would all tumble straight into the water! She had to open her eyes to see where her feet were going. They all had reached the bottom safely. Already, those at the head of the line were turning and scrambling up the side for another race down.

To her surprise, Eleanor found that she was struggling back up the hill, right behind the others. For the first time in her life she was doing something she thought was dangerous, without a sense of fear. Uncle Ted had said, "The first time is the hardest." Maybe some day, after all, she would learn to swim. Maybe some day she would learn not to be so afraid of so many things.

Today would be a precious memory for her to carry back to Grandmother Hall's. She would tuck it away among the other moments of happiness to come in these few short days with Uncle Ted and his family. In the gray, quiet days of fall and winter ahead, she could bring forth her memories and live them over again.

Visits at Sagamore Hill were the briefest of times for Eleanor in a life that had become filled with lessons— school lessons, music lessons, dancing lessons. Almost without notice in the big, formal home, the birthdays slipped by. Eleanor was eleven. Eleanor was twelve. Eleanor was thirteen and still growing.

Shyly, Eleanor tried reaching out to the people around her. They were all grown ups. Grandmother Hall was very strict about playmates. She did not consider the children of Eleanor's age in the neighborhood "suitable" for Eleanor.

Eleanor tried to make up for this by being helpful to the grown ups around her. Whenever Grandmother Hall would allow it, Eleanor trailed after her. She would listen to the instructions Mrs. Hall gave cook for the day's meals, then race off to help. She was just as eager to do any errands for her aunts and uncles.

Her older relatives seemed to take pity on the lonely young girl and did their best to include Eleanor in their plans. Aunt Pussie even allowed Eleanor to come along when she went buggy riding with her boy friend of the moment. Uncle Vallie took time to show Eleanor how to improve her horseback riding. She tried very hard to be a good rider. She knew how much her father had loved sports.

Often Eleanor followed the servants about, trying to fill the hours. She liked to think that she was helping to make things easy for them. The servants always seemed to have so much to do. Eleanor would help Kitty, the chamber maid, make the beds. She would help Victor dry the dishes.

Once her Aunt Maude found Eleanor folding some pillow cases with Kitty, and took Eleanor aside. "You silly girl, what are you going to learn from servants?" her aunt scolded her. "You would do better to watch how Pussie fixes her hair, so you can catch a man some day."

"I got up early and I didn't have anything to do," Eleanor explained. "Madeleine won't let me read before breakfast," she added, with a sigh.

"Madeleine is only following instructions," Maude told her. "Your grandmother thinks you will ruin your eyes reading in bed early in the morning."

Eleanor hesitated. "Do you like Madeleine?" she asked suddenly.

Maude laughed. "You don't have to like a servant. She's supposed to help you."

Eleanor bit her fingernail. "Madeleine doesn't like me," she said quickly, glancing over her shoulder.

"Aren't you being foolish, Eleanor?"

"Really, Aunt Maude," Eleanor insisted. "Grandmother says Madeleine must brush my hair every night. She pulls it so hard, it almost makes me cry."

But Aunt Maude wasn't inclined to take Eleanor seriously. "Oh, that reminds me," she said. "Pussie is sick in bed with a cold. Her eyes are watering and her nose is running. She feels terrible."

"Is there anything I can do?" Eleanor asked.

"Yes," Maude went on. "I'm going to the opera this evening, and it's the servants' night out. If Pussie needs anything, will you help her? I don't want Grandmother disturbed."

Eleanor tried to keep herself awake that night to be sure that she would hear if her aunt called. She was just about asleep when she heard her name.

Without stopping to put on her bedroom slippers, Eleanor raced across the cold floor. "What do you want, Aunt Pussie?" she asked.

"Eleanor, would you please get me some ice? Sucking on ice helps my throat. I had a bowl of it by my bed, but it's all melted."

The girl's heart began to pound. It was after midnight. The ice was stored in an icebox in the back yard. The only way she could get it was to go out through the basement door, which was three flights down.

"Would you hurry, Eleanor? My throat is burning up."

Eleanor turned. She could feel the goose flesh rising on her arms. She started down the first flight of stairs slowly, then stopped. She couldn't go on. She would have to go back and tell Pussie she would get her any-thing—anything at all, except the ice out in the darkness of the back yard.

There wasn't the least bit of light in the lower floor of the house. Eleanor was afraid of the dark, imagining burglars leaping at her out of the shadows. Surely, Pus-sie would understand? They both knew how a thief had stolen Grandmother Hall's jewelry one night!

Eleanor held on to the cold wooden stair rail, her ears alert. She heard Pussie turn over in bed. Eleanor took another step down. Pussie needed help. It was up to her to get the ice.

Driven by fear, Eleanor raced down to the basement and out to the yard. She flew back to the quiet safety of

Pussie's room with the ice. She could have shouted for joy.

"Eleanor, you are a dear girl," her aunt said. "I don't know what I would have done without you."

Still shaking, Eleanor scrambled back into bed. Her aunt's words sang in her ears. More important, she had conquered fear, at least this once.

When they went to Grandmother Hall's summer home the next year, Eleanor found she liked most being with the servants there. Mrs. Overhalse, the woman who did the laundry, would often give Eleanor some simple tasks to do. One day Grandmother Hall was walking on the lawn. She glanced into the laundry and noticed Eleanor ironing some napkins.

"Eleanor," her grandmother called, "I'm going for a walk in the woods. I'd like some company. Please come along."

As they set off, her grandmother said, "I think it's fine for you to learn all about household tasks. But try not to take up the servants' time and get in their way."

"Mrs. Overhalse says I iron very well," Eleanor told her proudly. "And Victor lets me dry the very best china."

Her grandmother smiled. "Well, I must say the servants do like you."

"All except one," Eleanor burst out, then stopped.

Her grandmother looked at her sharply. "Go on, child, let's hear the rest of what you were going to say."

"All except Madeleine," Eleanor confessed. In a swift tumble of words, Eleanor admitted how afraid she was of the French maid.

Grandmother Hall gazed at Eleanor in surprise. "Why didn't you tell me sooner, child? I would have done something at once. I will get another maid for you immediately."

Eleanor felt a sudden weight lift from her heart.

"Why was I afraid to tell her before?" she thought. Had it been because she felt her grandmother didn't love her? Maybe underneath her grandmother's cold manner there was love, after all. Could Eleanor have been too blind—too frightened—to see it?

Shyly, Eleanor reached for her grandmother's hand. "It is good being here with you," she began, trying to put her feelings into words. "Hall and I are grateful—"

"Nonsense, child," her grandmother interrupted. "There is no need for thanks. You children are my responsibility."

Eleanor sighed. The magic moment for saying "I love you, Grandmother," had passed.

They walked on in silence. Eleanor wished that her grandmother would stop calling her "child."

Eleanor glanced down at her dress, its skirt high above her knees. That was another thing which she had kept silent about far too long. Eleanor realized that it was hard to find suitable clothes for a girl almost six feet tall. Very often her aunts' clothes would be made over for her. But most of the time her grandmother insisted on dressing her like a little girl, which only made her look twice as tall and clumsy. All the other girls Eleanor knew wore their dresses down to their ankles, in the style of the day.

"Cat got your tongue?" her grandmother asked Eleanor.

Eleanor walked on silently. How could she get her grandmother to realize she had left her childhood behind?

CHAPTER 6

The Magic Secret

Eleanor sat on the window seat in her room, the pale winter sunlight falling across the letter she was reading. It was from Aunt Corinne, her father's youngest sister.

"It would please me very much if you could visit us during the holidays," her aunt wrote. "As you know, we always have a big Christmas dance for all the young people in the family. Your cousins see so little of you, they are all looking forward eagerly to having you with us. Please do try to come!"

Did she want to go? In a way she did, very much—things were always so gay, so beautiful at Aunt Corinne's house. There, everyone seemed always happy.

But then . . . Eleanor let the letter fall to her lap. Perhaps it wouldn't be much fun, after all. There was that party she had gone to at cousin Susie's last year—that party where nobody asked her for a single dance! She felt a little sick, remembering that dreadful, endless evening. The others had all enjoyed themselves. She could hear again the little jokes, the laughter. She could see the whirling, smiling couples on the dance floor.

"But I might as well have been invisible that night," Eleanor reminded herself. "Why, hardly anyone even spoke to me. I couldn't go through another evening like that one!"

She picked up the letter again. At the end, Aunt Corinne had added, "Cousin Alice will be here, of course, and many others you know." Having cousin Alice there would be a help, Eleanor thought. She was so pretty and so popular that a little of her beauty and charm seemed to rub off on those around her.

"I want to go," Eleanor told herself. And then, almost in the same breath, "No—no, I don't! Not unless I could somehow be at least six inches shorter, and—and pretty! Not unless somehow, between now and then, I could learn how to have fun!"

She got to her feet. She had forgotten something—the decision was not hers to make. Grandmother Hall would make it in any case, so why worry about it in advance? With a little sigh, Eleanor took Aunt Corinne's letter and went in search of her grandmother.

"She will say no," Eleanor guessed, as her grandmother read the letter. Grandmother Hall practically always said

59

no to any suggestion which came from the Roosevelt side of the family.

Eleanor's grandmother put the letter aside. She was smiling. "It sounds as if it will be a lovely party," she said. "You may go."

She had been so ready to plead against her grandmother's refusing to let her go that now Eleanor could find nothing to say. She managed a "Thank you, Grandmother," and fled back to her room. Now she *had* to go to Aunt Corinne's party!

To keep from thinking about the party itself, Eleanor turned her thoughts to why Grandmother Hall had said yes—so quickly, so easily, without even stopping to consider! Was it, Eleanor wondered, because Theodore Roosevelt had become such a very important man?

She remembered the visit to Sagamore Hill, when she was ten. So much had happened to Uncle Ted since then! "So very much," Eleanor thought, "in the same four years in which practically nothing at all has happened to me!"

It was now 1898, the year of the Spanish-American War—the war for Cuba's independence from Spain. When the United States went into the war, on the side of Cuba, Theodore Roosevelt had offered to raise a regiment. A group of men from all walks of life had joined him. There were men from the social world, many of them Uncle Ted's personal friends. And there were other friends of Uncle Ted's, too—rough-living cowboys from the days he had spent out West.

Theodore Roosevelt had been made a colonel and put in charge of a company that quickly earned the name "Rough Riders." Eleanor had seen newspaper pictures of Uncle Ted in his uniform, looking big and solid enough to win a war all by himself.

A most important battle of the war, Eleanor knew from those same newspapers, was the successful attack on San Juan Hill, in Cuba. It had been led by Colonel Roosevelt. In a few months, Uncle Ted had become famous as the hero of San Juan Hill, and his Rough Riders had become a legend.

How wonderful it must be, Eleanor dreamed, to be cousin Alice—the daughter of Colonel Roosevelt. Now he was Governor Roosevelt of New York State. He had been elected last November, swept into office on the tide of his war record. The Roosevelts were living in the Governor's home in Albany, New York.

And Eleanor was going to a party where the Governor's daughter would also be a guest. Like it or not, she was going to the party. "I will like it," Eleanor promised herself, day dreaming. "It won't be like that other time. I will dance every dance, and somehow I will know exactly what to say to the boys, so that they will think I'm charming and full of fun, like cousin Alice! I will have fun."

The dream faded. Such things didn't happen by magic! What had Uncle Ted told her, that long-ago day when she had been afraid to go swimming? *Give it a try—just this once.*

"All right," Eleanor told herself. "I will give it a try. But I need help."

She thought about her Aunt Pussie, always so popular at parties. Perhaps there was some simple, almost-magic secret that her aunt would share. It wouldn't hurt to find out. She went to look for Aunt Pussie.

"What will I say?" Eleanor asked her aunt. "I'm afraid to talk to boys. I never know what to talk about."

"I'll give you a fool-proof way to start a conversation," Aunt Pussie told her. "Just go through the alphabet. Pick a subject that begins with A. *Do you like apples, Mr. Smith?* When you have finished with the subject of apples, go on to B. *Have you been to Baltimore, Mr. Smith?* And so on."

"Will it work?" Eleanor asked, not sure her aunt wasn't teasing her.

"Like a charm," Aunt Pussie assured her.

When Eleanor arrived at Aunt Corinne's house, it was already filled with young people. A maid took Eleanor's suitcase and led her to the bedroom she was to share with several other girls.

Eleanor took her clothes out at once. She didn't want her party dress to be wrinkled. As she went to hang her dress in the closet, she gasped with surprise. Several other dresses were already hanging there—pale, fluffy gowns with lovely sashes and delicate lace. As she hung up her own dress, Eleanor saw with dismay that hers was much shorter than the rest—and she was so much taller than any of the other girls! Her dress looked like a school girl's uniform hanging there among those pretty fluffy gowns.

Sinking down in a chair by the window, Eleanor buried her face in her hands. In imagination, she lived through the terrible evening she would have to endure, wearing that awful dress!

She was surprised by a knock at the door. Then her cousin Alice came bouncing in, her cheeks rosy, her eyes sparkling. She was wearing a very smart red-and-white skating outfit.

"Eleanor, do hurry!" Alice urged. "We are waiting for you to go skating with us!"

"Skating?" Eleanor drew back in her chair. Things were getting worse by the minute! She could hardly stand up on skates.

"I didn't bring any skates," she said weakly.

"No matter," Alice told her cheerfully. "We can borrow a pair for you."

Eleanor stood up and went over to her cousin. "Alice, I'm a dreadful skater. You see, I have weak ankles, and—"

"Nonsense!" Alice had already turned toward the door. "Just give it a try. You know, the way Daddy always says to do!" Alice hurried out.

Eleanor struggled into her winter coat—one of Aunt Pussie's that had been made over for her. As she went downstairs and outdoors, she held on to one last hope: Alice might not be able to find skates to fit her.

But the hope faded as soon as Eleanor caught up with the others at the small pond in the woods. Alice had borrowed a pair of boys skates! Eleanor could see, without even trying them on, that they would be large enough.

Slowly, she put on the skates. She stood up, not at all steady on her feet. With a sinking heart, she realized that the skates made her look even more tall and clumsy than she was.

Her arms swinging wildly in an effort to keep her balance, Eleanor managed to reach the edge of the pond. Her blades had hardly touched the ice when she slipped and fell flat—all six feet of her stretched out on the ice!

Alice and the others hurried over to help. Eleanor struggled to her feet, waving them away. "I'm all right," she panted. "I think I will just sit down for a while."

She staggered to a log and took off the skates. She had torn her long black stockings and skinned her knee.

Eleanor looked back toward the house. It was too soon to go in—Aunt Corinne would be worried that she wasn't having a good time. For a long while she sat there, the cold biting into her. Finally she could stand it no longer. Her lips were blue, her hands frozen.

Getting up stiffly, Eleanor went back to the house. She heard the sound of pots and pans in the kitchen as she started slowly up the stairs. Even in the bedroom, the sharp, tickling smell of spices filled the air.

Eleanor drew back the curtains and looked out. She

saw a line of boys and girls coasting down a hill. There was still a number of people skating on the pond. Eleanor turned away. She picked up a book and began to read.

It seemed as if the day would never end. And she had yet to face the evening dance, the high spot of the Christmas holidays!

That evening, Eleanor found excuses to take up her time while the other girls—beautifully dressed and bright-eyed—went down to the big drawing room. Finally Eleanor was left alone. Each time the door bell echoed through the house, she jumped. She heard the orchestra tune up. "Perhaps Aunt Corinne will be too busy to notice that I'm not there." Eleanor tried to comfort herself—but she didn't believe it.

Soon cousin Alice came hurrying into the bedroom. "Oh, thank goodness! You've dressed!" she cried, out of breath from the stairs. "I wondered what was keeping you so long. Do hurry, Eleanor! They have already started dancing."

Her lively chatter died away as she stared at Eleanor's short, plain dress. She must have understood, for she came across and took Eleanor's hand. "Don't worry," she comforted. "The people down there are all friendly. It's Christmas. You are going to have a wonderful time!"

They went downstairs together. As soon as the boys caught sight of Alice, they came rushing. She was whirled off to the dance floor.

Eleanor hesitated, then chose a quiet corner and went

over to lose herself in it. She tried to shrink back—but how could she hide when she towered over all of the girls and most of the boys? "If only I could make myself invisible!" she thought sadly.

"Pardon me," said a voice at her side. Eleanor turned. There stood a tall, handsome blond young man with a wide smile. He was Eleanor's 16-year-old cousin, Franklin Delano Roosevelt.

"Why, Franklin, you've come a long way from Hyde Park," Eleanor said, too surprised for a moment to be shy.

"Mother and I are spending the holidays in New York City," he explained. "Have you heard—I'm going to Groton!"

Eleanor nodded. Groton was a famous boarding school for boys, in Massachusetts. But what could she say about it to Franklin? *That's nice* was all she could think of—but that would sound pretty flat . . .

Franklin didn't seem to notice Eleanor's silence. Politely, he put out his hand. "Would you like to dance?" he asked.

Eleanor's heart leaped. All at once she found herself in Franklin's arms, and he was leading her easily about the dance floor. She was dancing! She was part of the fun! She was—why, she was having a wonderful time!

When the dance was over, Franklin started to return her to her corner. Eleanor took a deep breath. "Franklin," she said boldly, "do you like apples?"

He turned to her with his bright smile. "Why, yes. There are some delicious apples in a bowl over there. Shall we have some?"

"It works," Eleanor thought. "It really works. I know the magic secret!"

CHAPTER 7

"You Are a True Roosevelt"

"What are you reading?"

Uncle Ted's voice surprised Eleanor out of her day dream. She looked up at him with a happy smile. It was wonderful to be back here at Sagamore Hill, her favorite place in the world, sitting in her favorite chair on the wide porch, reading a favorite book. She couldn't ask for more.

She must enjoy every precious moment of the visit. Next fall she would be going away to Allenswood, a school in England. This might be her last visit with Uncle Ted and his family for a long, long time.

Theodore Roosevelt pulled over one of the rush-bottomed chairs and sat down next to his 15-year-old niece. "What are you reading, Eleanor?" he asked again. "Some book for fun?" His eyes twinkled. "Or something to improve your mind?"

"It's a novel," Eleanor said shyly. "I have read it before. It's not a really great book, like something by Dickens or Sir Walter Scott. But"—she looked out over the sparkling waters of the bay—"it's a sad story. I don't know why I like it so much, really." Her hands fluttered nervously. "It makes me cry every time . . ." Her voice faded away.

Uncle Ted nodded with understanding. They sat quietly for a few moments. How pleasant time spent with her uncle could be—even when neither of them said a word! With Uncle Ted, silence was a friendly thing, and all the silent words which filled it were kindly, gentle words.

Although she loved her cousin, she was sorry when Alice appeared in the doorway, saying, "Who wants to go swimming?"

"Not I," said Eleanor, and "I do," said Uncle Ted, both in the same breath.

They laughed. "Get into your suit anyway," Uncle Ted suggested. "It will be nice and cool down by the water."

A short time later, they all gathered in the big front hall, from baby Quentin—the newest addition to the Roosevelt family—on up to Alice. Off they marched for what Uncle Ted assured Eleanor would be a quiet swim. To make certain, Eleanor had her book along.

To her surprise, it *was* quiet. All the boys and girls

raced off into the water, leaving Eleanor alone. Even Quentin splashed happily at the water's edge.

"Still haven't learned to swim?" That was Uncle Ted. He dropped down beside Eleanor.

She shook her head.

"Some day you will," her uncle assured her. "Some day something will happen that will be bigger and more important than your fear—and you will learn to swim."

"I hope so." Eleanor hesitated a moment. Then she found the courage to add, "There is so much I must learn not to fear!"

Uncle Ted picked up the broken branch of an elm tree that lay on the beach. With the point of the stick, he began to draw a picture in the sand. It took on the shape of some animal with horns, but Eleanor wasn't sure what it was.

"Buffalo," her uncle said, putting down the stick. Suddenly he reached across and took the book from Eleanor's lap. He snapped it shut. "That isn't for you, Eleanor. You have too much of the fighting spirit in you."

"Fighting spirit?" Eleanor repeated.

"Yes. You have an open heart and mind. I can see it in you." He looked away for a moment at the children in the water. Then he turned back. "You are a true Roosevelt. Your mother and father would have been proud of you. You will see, Eleanor. When I was young, nobody knew that I had the fighting spirit, either."

Uncle Ted went on to tell Eleanor about his early

childhood, when he had been sick and spent a great deal of time in bed. He told how he used to watch the other boys playing outside, and how much he had wanted to be out there with them.

Her uncle fell silent, lost in his own thoughts. How gently this big, strong man spoke about his childhood. And about the growing-up years that had been so difficult—those same growing-up years that Eleanor, in a different way, was finding so difficult.

When Uncle Ted began to speak again, he talked of the time he had spent out West, many years later, after the death of his first wife. Eleanor knew that her uncle had written many articles about the excitement of living

in the Dakota territory, in what had been a wilderness at that time.

He told her now about the Indians, the cowboys, the buffalo and deer that roamed freely across the plains, the bear that stalked in the mountains.

"It was no place for a city man," Uncle Ted told her.

Eleanor smiled. But he *had* been a city man—he had made a place for himself in that different world. He had thrown himself into the rough frontier life with a will and with his whole heart.

"I ran away, when I went out West," Mr. Roosevelt said. "I ran away to escape." He was silent a moment. "Eleanor, there is no escape," he went on at last, looking at her closely. "I ran away, but I had to come back. I had to face life. Everyone has to, sooner or later."

Eleanor knew that her uncle was not talking about himself any longer. He was talking about her.

"I went out West frightened, scared. And I came back strong . . ." his eyes held hers—"because I had learned I had to do what must be done. It will happen to you, too," he finished, his voice strong and full of confidence.

Eleanor didn't know what to say. So few people spoke of personal matters to her. No one exchanged confidences with her. Even with her aunts, there was a bridge she could not cross. But here, on this beach, Uncle Ted had been able to make her feel as if they were by themselves in a secret world.

Eleanor glanced down at the rough drawing of the buffalo in the sand. It made her think of the huge buffalo head which was proudly displayed over the fireplace in the dining room of the Sagamore Hill house.

Uncle Ted had killed the buffalo when he was out West. She had never paid much attention to the stuffed animal head before. But now she knew why it meant so much to her uncle. It was a sign of courage. It had given him the strength to face the world without fear.

"Say, look there!" Her uncle put his hand on Eleanor's shoulder, in great excitement. "Isn't that an oyster catcher?" He pointed to a bird with a black head and long bill that was paddling along at the edge of the bay. "Haven't seen one of those around in years."

Eleanor stared at the bird. "I don't know. I don't know very much about birds."

"Well, you can learn," her uncle said. "Studying about birds and nature helped me through some of my worst days. I learned to bring the outdoors inside." He peered at Eleanor through his thick, gold-rimmed glasses for a long time. "I have weak eyes," he said suddenly. "Very weak. Sometimes it makes it hard for me to see people." He took Eleanor's thin hand in his. "So I've learned how to see through people."

Alice came running toward them, her lean, tanned body dripping with water. A black and white puppy scampered along at her heels. "Oh, Eleanor," Alice cried out, flinging herself down in the sand, "you should have come in. The water's great."

She pulled up the long skirt of the bathing suit and squeezed some of the water from the bottom edges, exposing the bloomers underneath the suit.

"When are you going to start acting like a young lady?" Uncle Ted laughed, pouring sand on Alice's back.

"When are you going to act like the Governor of New York?" Alice laughed, hugging her father. "Maybe when you get to be Vice President—"

Mr. Roosevelt shook his finger at Alice. "Miss Big Ears, you've been listening at keyholes."

"I have not," Alice said quickly. "It's common talk. It's in the newspapers. Lots of people would like you to run for Vice President." She paused. "Even President!"

She tickled her father under the chin. "Admit it."

Eleanor gazed at her uncle and cousin Alice. What a warm feeling it gave her to listen to Alice joke back and forth with her father—as if he were her friend!

Uncle Ted told Alice, "Eleanor is going to a fancy school in England. When she comes back, with proud airs, she most likely will never talk to you or me—unless I *am* President of the United States."

"Oh, no, that's not true," Eleanor put in quickly. "I would never—"

"I was only teasing," Uncle Ted answered her. "You should find school in England very interesting. Auntie Bye liked Allenswood very much. Your mother, if she were alive, would have wanted you to go to school abroad." He stood up, brushing the sand from his baggy swimming suit. There was a twinkle in his eye. "You will learn a great deal there. You may even see a sea pie."

"A sea pie?" Alice asked, wrinkling her nose. "You are making that up."

"No, I'm not," Uncle Ted said, tickling Alice's bare feet. "A sea pie is the name used in Europe for the oyster catcher. We saw one while you were swimming."

Alice put her arm around Eleanor. "You must write to us often. And you must write me right away if you ever get to see Queen Victoria of England."

"I will," Eleanor promised. "But there probably will be only dull things to tell."

Her uncle waved to the children still playing in the water. "Come on out," he shouted. "Last one up the hill is a rotten egg."

Eleanor shook the sand from her wool swimming suit. She slapped at a mosquito that kept buzzing around her, and crushed it against her leg.

Mr. Roosevelt turned to Eleanor. "What would you like to do now? How about a run down Cooper's Bluff —for old times' sake?"

"Oh, no," Eleanor laughed, shaking her head. "Not that. Not today."

Her uncle bent over in a funny bow. "Anything you say."

"I'd like to settle for a story up in the gun room," Eleanor suggested.

The gun room was a huge room on the top floor of the Sagamore Hill house. It had wide windows which looked out over the woods and the water of the bay. The gun room was a play room for the children. It had been designed as a hide-away for Theodore Roosevelt, but he had learned not to hide away, and now it was usually filled with young people. Here, sitting on a rug of beaver skins, facing a collection of guns and swords and dueling pistols on the wall, the children would gather. They would listen, wide-eyed, as Theodore Roosevelt told them jungle stories and recited some of his favorite poems by Rudyard Kipling.

"The gun room, the gun room," Quentin seconded,

running out of the water. He threw his arms around his father's legs.

Mr. Roosevelt swung the boy up on his shoulders. "Off we go to hunt lions in Africa!" He stooped down and picked up the elm branch from the sand. "Charge!" he bellowed. Young Ted, Kermit, Ethel and Archie flocked out of the water, laughing and panting. They fell into line behind their father.

Eleanor lagged behind her cousins as they walked up the path through the trees that led from the beach to the house. It was wonderful, sharing these precious few days with her uncle and his family. It was wonderful to have him hug her until she was out of breath and to tell her how "bully fine" she looked. But it was also sad. In the midst of fun, Eleanor suddenly felt very lonely.

CHAPTER 8

"Be Like the Bird"

Could this be the famous Allenswood School that Auntie Bye had picked for her? Everything was Do This or Don't Do That. Do make your bed every morning. Do be on time for every class. Do go for a walk each morning and never mind if the weather is cold or wet and nasty. Do speak French at all times except in English or other language classes.

Rules! It would be just as though she were still living at Grandmother Hall's.

The schedule of classes that Eleanor was given did nothing to cheer her. She had so many courses that the only time left for her to practice the piano was before breakfast. There were history, Italian and classes in English literature. There were German and Latin. Her afternoons were filled with music lessons and two hours of physical exercise. Studies began after dinner and lasted until lights out.

There was one benefit. Eleanor had no time left to feel sorry for herself. And, as the weeks sped by, she found that she was enjoying the heavy work load. Best of all, she discovered why Auntie Bye had chosen Allenswood. The secret was in the school's head mistress, Miss Souvestre. In this teacher, Eleanor began to find a friend and, in many ways, the mother she had never really known.

One evening after dinner, Miss Souvestre motioned to Eleanor to remain seated after the other students had left. "I'd like to see you in my study this evening promptly at eight," Miss Souvestre said. She nodded her silver head. "You may go now."

Eleanor went to her room with a sinking heart. She found Marjorie, her room mate, studying quietly. Eleanor sat down on the edge of the bed, her shoulders drooping. If only Miss Souvestre had told her what she had done that was wrong!

Marjorie glanced up. "What happened?" she asked, turning around in her chair. "Your face looks like a disaster. I thought you'd be thrilled to get an invitation."

"Invitation?" Eleanor looked puzzled.

"That is why Miss Souvestre asked you to stay after dinner, isn't it?" Marjorie went on. Then Marjorie explained that sometimes Miss Souvestre would invite a few girls for a literary evening. They would gather in Miss Souvestre's private study and she would read favorite poems and stories aloud to them.

"Four of us have been invited for tonight," Marjorie continued. "I'm going, and—"

Eleanor sank back with a sigh of relief. "I was afraid that I had done something terribly wrong!"

A few minutes before eight that evening, Eleanor went to Miss Souvestre's pleasant study. She and the other girls pulled chairs up close to the fireplace. They sat in a half-circle, with Miss Souvestre at one side. The head mistress held an open book on her lap, and there were several others piled on a table near her.

Eleanor sat happily while Miss Souvestre read aloud. The teacher's voice sounded to Eleanor like music. She recited poems by romantic poets from the Middle Ages and stirring passages of social protest by popular writers of the day. She acted out a funny scene from one of Molière's plays and then read a sharply biting passage from the novel *Candide*. Everything seemed to interest the silver-haired teacher.

After reading awhile, Miss Souvestre discussed with the girls the authors she liked and why she liked them. In this way she reminded Eleanor of her father.

There was a quiet, peaceful quality about the passing hours. Suddenly, the sound of a log falling in the fireplace surprised Eleanor. And then Miss Souvestre spoke her name, bringing her back to earth.

"Can you repeat the Victor Hugo poem I just read?"

Eleanor realized that her attention had been wandering . . . and yet her ears had been alert.

"I don't know." Eleanor hesitated. Then she took a deep breath.

> *Be like the bird,*
> *Who halting in his flight . . .*
> *On limb too slight*
> *Feels it give way beneath him.*

Eleanor's voice slowed for a moment, then lifted as she remembered the end.

> *Yet sings*
> *Knowing he hath wings.*

Marjorie, who was seated next to Eleanor, began to clap. The other girls joined in. Miss Souvestre wore a pleased smile.

"It is good advice for you, Eleanor. For all of us. *Be like the bird.*"

There were other literary evenings just as pleasant. Eleanor had many chances to show off her remarkable memory, often repeating the poem which Miss Souvestre had just read.

Miss Souvestre and Allenswood were wakening a love of learning in Eleanor. More important, the shy 15-year-old was learning to take pride in herself. A small spark of confidence was beginning to glow in Eleanor. The world was not as frightening as she had thought.

Many of the students at Allenswood were as far away from home as Eleanor, some even farther. A few girls came from India and Australia. Miss Souvestre knew how home sick a girl could be at boarding school. She made it her business to keep a close watch on all her students.

Each evening, before bed time, the girls met in the library. It was a beautiful room, filled with books. Miss Souvestre loved to fill the room with vases of flowers in season. The delicate scent of her French perfume blended with that of the flowers.

The short, plump head mistress sat quietly in an arm-chair while her assistant, Miss Samaia, gave each girl her mail. Miss Souvestre then stood up and kissed each girl good night.

One evening, Miss Souvestre noticed that for the second day in a row, Eleanor had not received any mail.

"Mail from America is often delayed," Miss Souvestre said. "I am sure you will receive many letters tomorrow."

Eleanor was touched by Miss Souvestre's concern. "It really doesn't matter. I have my father's letters to read," Eleanor said. She stopped. Perhaps Miss Souvestre would not understand.

Miss Souvestre gave her a quick, puzzled look. "But your father is dead."

"These are letters he wrote to me a long time ago," Eleanor explained. "I keep them with me."

Miss Souvestre cleared her throat. "Miss Samaia tells me that you bite your nails." The change of subject was so sudden that Eleanor was not prepared to make any excuses.

"Yes," she admitted. "I have tried everything to make myself stop but I don't seem to be able to."

"Everything?" Miss Souvestre raised her eyebrows. "I doubt it. Think hard. There must be something that will help you to keep your nails long and pretty." She paused. "Think what your father would say."

In the quiet of her room that night, Eleanor began to read her father's letters slowly. She knew each line by heart now, yet seeing his handwriting made him seem closer to her. Suddenly, one line in a letter stood out. Strange, how she had passed it over before! Her father reminded her to make the most of her appearance—to care for each part of her body as if it were something precious. Thoughtfully, Eleanor put the letters away.

At the end of two weeks, Miss Souvestre took Eleanor's hand in hers. "Your nails are growing long. They are beautiful," she praised Eleanor. "See? If you make up your mind, you can do anything!"

During Christmas and Easter vacations many of the students were not able to return to their homes. Special plans had to be made for those who lived far away.

For her first Christmas at school, it was arranged that Eleanor would go to Paris to stay with Madame Bertaux, a French woman, and her two daughters. Eleanor was thrilled. The holiday would give her a brief chance to be on her own.

At first, Eleanor felt ill at ease with the Bertaux family. The small apartment was clean but the furniture was heavy and the chair cushions over-stuffed, like sausages. There was no running water in Eleanor's room. Morning and evening, a maid came with a pitcher of hot water to be used for washing.

The meals Madame Bertaux prepared tasted strange to Eleanor. They also seemed rather small. Sometimes a bowl of cabbage and peas would be the main dish. When she went with her to market, Eleanor noticed that Madame Bertaux counted each penny she spent on food.

But Madame Bertaux was hearty and friendly. Her daughters were intelligent, and helped Eleanor with her French. Soon Eleanor was feeling more like a member of the family.

Even the food began to taste delicious. Eleanor realized that Madame Bertaux was a master at disguising cheap, tough cuts of meat by flavoring them with spices and wines and cooking them very slowly. She learned to eat onion soup and rabbit stew and hard cheese and to love every bit of it.

Once they had a special kind of soup, and Eleanor asked Madame Bertaux how it was made. "It is a soup eaten by the peasant for many, many years," Madame Bertaux told her. "It is made with pieces of salt pork for flavor. Who knows just what goes in it? My mother showed me how to make it on my wedding morning." Madame Bertaux smiled, her plump red cheeks creased into wrinkles. "I think of it as my wedding-day soup."

One of her daughters laughed. "We call it the copper-pot soup, because that's what Mama makes it in."

"It is still wedding-day soup to me," Madame Bertaux said. "That copper pot was the only present my mother was able to give me."

Eleanor felt as if Paris were a special gift given to her. It was a place of never-ending wonder. Each day she would be taken to another part of the city. Eleanor never seemed to tire, so the Bertaux sisters took turns taking her sight-seeing.

Eleanor walked down the Champs Élysées and stared at the lovely shops, grand hotels and charming restaurants along the wide avenue. It reminded her a little of New York's Fifth Avenue. As she strolled, she stopped often to peer into small shops where artists showed and sold their paintings.

She saw all of the famous places that visitors in Paris usually go to see. She climbed the Eiffel Tower, where she got a dizzying view of the city. She went to the Louvre, where she stood for a long time in front of Leonardo da Vinci's painting, the *Mona Lisa*.

"It is magnificent," Eleanor said. "I thought I would be disappointed in the *Mona Lisa*. You know, you expect so much from something you hear about. Then, when you do finally get to see it, you are often let down. But this painting—" She spread out her hands, unable to find words to describe the famous *Mona Lisa*.

"Ah, but that is because you are looking at the painting with your heart as well as your eyes. Come! There is much to see besides museums."

The bright Paris sunlight warmed them as they came out of the hush of the Louvre. "It is too nice to be indoors any more today," Eleanor suggested. "Let's walk along the Seine."

They strolled along the right bank of the Seine, the river which flows through Paris. They stopped near a man who was fishing at the water's edge. They paused to watch an artist who was painting a picture of Notre Dame Cathedral.

"Everything is so beautiful in Paris," Eleanor said.

"Visitors never get to see the dirt in a city, the poor people . . ." Miss Bertaux told her.

"Will you take me to see the poor—the other side of Paris?" Eleanor asked.

"I don't know. Perhaps one day."

Miss Bertaux made a sharp turn around a corner. "Let's go see Les Halles now. I know it is already too late for most of the excitement. You have to come very early, five or six o'clock in the morning, to see the farmers bringing in their vegetables, and the butchers hanging up freshly killed pigs and sheep. Let's go anyway."

And there it was, stretched out before them—Les Halles, the food market of Paris. From here, food was sent to all parts of Paris—into the restaurants, the grocery stores and the homes.

The streets were littered with lettuce leaves. Squashed tomatoes lay on the ground. Eleanor picked her way among the vegetable stalls and fish counters.

Then suddenly, as they walked on, a delicious smell was carried on the breeze. Eleanor stopped in front of a shop. The owner was putting out trays of pastries on a paper-lined counter. There were cream puffs, lemon tarts and chocolate cakes with fresh frosting melting down the sides.

Eleanor could sense the rich taste of the chocolate in her mouth. She glanced at her friend but the young woman had already walked ahead. Eleanor hurried to catch up with her. "Please, wait a moment," Eleanor said. She pointed back to the pastry shop. "I would like to get some. When I was young—" She stopped. Eleanor didn't want to spoil the happiness of the moment by thinking of the past.

Her companion nodded. "Ah, yes," she said. "You were perhaps too poor to enjoy much pastry when you were young."

They went back. Eleanor could not make up her mind which pastry to select. Finally, she said to the owner in his white apron, "*Deux.*" She held up two fingers. She pointed to two pastries. He gave them to her in small paper cups. Eleanor handed one to her friend. They walked along the river bank again, nibbling.

"I would never do this at home," Eleanor said.

"Do what?"

"Eat in the street."

"But why not?" the other girl laughed.

"My grandmother would say it isn't proper." Eleanor's blue eyes sparkled, then she popped her fingers into her mouth and sucked off some cake crumbs. "But it is fun," she said, swallowing the last bite.

CHAPTER 9

The Red Dress

Each day at Allenswood brought fresh delight to Eleanor.

She was chosen to sit opposite Miss Souvestre at the dining-room table. This was a great privilege—and a great responsibility. It meant she would be constantly under the eyes of the head mistress.

But Eleanor didn't mind. Often Miss Souvestre invited important guests to dine with her. Eleanor listened eagerly to the interesting table talk, learning about events and ideas that were new to her. Later she was to make use, in her own conversations, of much that she learned at Miss Souvestre's table.

Eleanor began to feel important. Her school mates had to wait for her signal before they could be dismissed at the end of each meal. For many years Eleanor had always stood quietly in the background, all attention being given her beautiful mother. At Grandmother Hall's, Eleanor's aunts were always the center of attention. But at Allenswood, Eleanor was at last given a chance.

As pleasant as school life was, all of the students looked forward eagerly to vacations. Easter of 1901 was drawing near. No plans had been made for Eleanor. She wondered what she was going to do.

One lovely, warm spring afternoon, Miss Souvestre called Eleanor into her study. "How would you like to travel with me this holiday?" she asked the young girl.

Eleanor could not say "yes" fast enough. Then, gathering her thoughts, Eleanor asked Miss Souvestre where she planned to travel.

"Oh, wherever we wish," Miss Souvestre smiled.

Eleanor gazed at her in surprise. Surely, the school mistress was joking! Eleanor could not imagine traveling unless every detail was carefully planned and prepared for well ahead of time.

"We will go to Marseilles first," Miss Souvestre explained. "And then to Pisa . . . and Florence." Miss Souvestre threw out her hands. "We will go wherever there will be adventures for us." She sat back, her eyes bright. "You will be in charge of everything."

Eleanor had never been given such responsibility before. How could she possibly take care of all the details that were part of traveling?

"You will do it all—and do it all well," Miss Souvestre went on calmly. Eleanor shivered at the way Miss Souvestre had of reading her mind. "You will see Europe as you have never seen it before. And, Eleanor, you will *not* be afraid."

On most of her trips, Eleanor had had a maid to help her. Now Miss Souvestre insisted that she do the packing for both of them. Eleanor was the one who had to buy the train tickets. She was the one who had to check railroad schedules. She was the one who had to handle the foreign money.

Eleanor found, to her surprise and pleasure, that the more she was called upon to do, the more she was able to do. She realized what it meant to believe in herself. She learned not to be afraid. The world was fun. The world was beautiful. It didn't matter so much, now, if she herself were tall and thin and not attractive.

Miss Souvestre taught Eleanor more than how to enjoy traveling. She taught her to be ready for adventure.

They had spent several glorious days in France, and were now on their way to Italy. Eleanor had carefully checked all their travel arrangements. Their large trunks were safely in the baggage car of the train. She and Miss Souvestre had their own small suitcases with them.

Eleanor settled back as the train passed through the French country. It was getting toward dusk. The sun was sinking. Eleanor still sat at her window seat, watching the changing scene. French farms sped by. A church steeple poked above a cluster of little village roofs.

Miss Souvestre sat at Eleanor's side, sleeping. Her head bobbed from side to side when the train made a sudden turn.

The train pulled into a station. They had crossed the border. Now they were in Italy. The conductor shouted out, "Alassio. All out for Alassio!"

Miss Souvestre jumped to her feet. "My dear, we are getting out here," she said to Eleanor. She leaned over to pull open the window. "Wait a moment, please," she called to the conductor. "We are getting off."

Eleanor was too surprised to move. They were not supposed to get off at Alassio—they were on their way to Pisa! Eleanor didn't know anything at all about Alassio. Why in the world would Miss Souvestre want to stop here?

For a quick moment, Eleanor was reminded of her Aunt Pussie and her sudden ideas. But Miss Souvestre was not like that.

There was nothing for Eleanor to do but to follow after the school mistress. She quickly took the two bags and stumbled off the train, right behind Miss Souvestre. As the train pulled out of the station, Eleanor gasped, "Our trunks are on the train!"

"Be calm, my dear," Miss Souvestre said. "They will hold our trunks for us." She turned to Eleanor with a smile. "When I heard the name Alassio," she explained, "I remembered that I have a good friend here. I have

94

not seen her in a long time. It occurred to me, *when will I next be in Alassio? Perhaps never!*"

Eleanor continued to gaze at her seriously. Miss Souvestre added with a laugh, "You are young and you have fallen in love with France. Now I am going to help you fall in love with Italy. "Come along." She took Eleanor's hand.

In the evening light they walked to an empty beach. A small fishing boat with bright red sails was pulled up on the sand. The Mediterranean stretched out its blue waters to meet the black sky.

"Oh, it's so beautiful," Eleanor cried.

The old school mistress put her fingers to her lips. "Don't say anything. I want you to remember this place for the rest of your life."

When they turned from the beach, they found that Miss Souvestre's friend was not at home. They had to stay in a hotel which was being built. It was not quite finished, but the hotel keeper gave them a room.

Day by day, on their travels, Eleanor learned how to accept freely and without fear whatever life had to offer. She saw France and Italy in a way she had never believed possible. She learned how to travel with her eyes, her ears—and her heart.

Wherever they were they ate the foods of the country. In Marseilles, they tried fish soup, a special dish in that part of France. In Pisa, they drank red wine from grapes grown in the hills of the town. They spoke French in France, Italian in Italy and English hardly at all. In Florence, they lived in a house on top of a hill, from which they could see the city.

Each city had a charm of its own, and each opened Eleanor's world a little more. She had thought there could be few cities in the world to compare with the excitement of Paris. But when she saw Florence, she lost her heart again.

Eleanor had been studying the works of Dante at school. The great Italian writer had lived in Florence. Eleanor was thrilled to think that she was walking the same streets he had walked. Perhaps she was seeing the very same sights—for the beauty of Florence dates back hundreds of years.

It was spring. Eleanor was 16. Miss Souvestre was 70 years old. She had discovered the charm of the old city. Now it was Eleanor's turn.

Following breakfast, the day after they had arrived, Miss Souvestre took a guide book out of her huge purse. She put it in Eleanor's hands.

"Go," she said. "See Florence for yourself."

Eleanor was surprised. What would her grandmother say if she ever found out? No proper young lady who was not married went about all alone—especially not in a strange city!

"Walk, walk, walk!" Miss Souvestre was pushing Eleanor through the door. "It is the only way to see the city.

When you come back, we will have a talk about it."

Eleanor hung back. "But where shall I begin?" she asked. The prospect of the adventure excited her—and yet it frightened her, too. What if she got lost? Her knowledge of Italian was not all that good. What if—

"Go see the famous bell tower, first. All the visitors start there. And then"—Miss Souvestre laughed—"go anywhere. All Florence is an art museum."

Eleanor found that art was indeed everywhere. The outsides of buildings and churches, even the city government buildings, were as beautifully decorated as the insides. Eleanor lingered in the Pitti Palace, whose marble floors had once echoed with the royal steps of Italy's kings. Part of the palace was used as a museum, and it contained wonderful paintings by famous artists.

Eleanor walked through the Boboli Gardens, behind the palace. She thought they were as beautifully landscaped as the formal gardens in Paris. Toward evening, Eleanor walked over the Ponte Vecchio, a bridge built across the River Arno. It connected one part of Florence with the other. Eleanor remembered from studying history with Miss Souvestre that this famous bridge had been built by the Romans. Now she was delighted to wander into the many small shops which long ago had been built into the walls of the bridge. Here were displays of pottery and lovely jewelry. In some of the shops men sat patiently working delicate gold and silver wires into beautiful pieces of jewelry.

Eleanor looked at jewel boxes and vases, trying to make up her mind just what to buy. She knew that she would be going home from school that summer. She wanted to bring back some unusual souvenirs for her grandmother and aunts and for other family members.

Looking about her at all the beauty, Eleanor realized why she had fallen so quickly and completely under the spell of Florence. All this reminded her so much of the second time she had been in Paris.

Eleanor had loved each moment. The days were much too short. There were so many things to see. The formal gardens, the fountains, the wide avenues, the art galleries, the museums—everything delighted her.

When she arrived in Paris for her second visit, Eleanor had wondered if the city would still hold the same charm and excitement for her. She found that it did. And this time, a wonderful thing happened to Eleanor.

Miss Souvestre, who had been traveling during the Christmas holidays, stopped in Paris. When Eleanor came to see her, she talked on and on. At the end of her long, happy story of seeing Paris, Miss Souvestre waved her hand. "Enough, Eleanor, enough! You have told me of the great churches and museums here—but not one word about the dress shops!"

"Dress shops?" Eleanor looked blank.

"Of course! Women's clothes—that is another thing for which Paris is noted." Miss Souvestre pointed to the ruffled collar on Eleanor's dress. "Do you know when this went out of style?"

Eleanor was shocked. Of all people, surely Miss Souvestre would not make fun of her clothes! It was true, of course, that many of her aunts' dresses had been made over for Eleanor when her aunts had lost interest in them, or the fashions changed.

"You are hiding yourself under these hand-me-down clothes," Miss Souvestre said. "Miss Samaia is here with me. Tomorrow morning she will go with you to a fine dressmaker we know. You will have a dress made to order, just for you."

Eleanor looked worried. A dress made to order was expensive. She knew that her mother and her father had left money to her when they died—but her grandmother had never told her how much. Eleanor had always been given a small amount of spending money.

"Be careful with it," warned her grandmother. Mary Hall had seen how quickly her own children had spent the money left them, and she had made up her mind this was not going to happen to Eleanor.

Grandmother Hall, however, had sent Miss Souvestre money to pay for the cost of Eleanor's holiday in Paris. There was still enough money left, the head mistress assured Eleanor, so that she could treat herself to a dress —a brand-new dress, especially made for her.

Miss Souvestre, who understood Eleanor all too well, added one final instruction. "The dress must be red, Eleanor. No other color."

The next morning, Miss Samaia took Eleanor to a poor part of Paris. They turned down a narrow back alley and entered the dark hall of an old building. They walked up a long flight of creaking wooden steps to an attic room.

The dressmaker greeted them at the door. "Well," she said, sizing up Eleanor's tall, thin figure. "Well!" She turned Eleanor back and forth as if she were a wooden doll. Then, suddenly, the dressmaker began pulling out bolts of material from closets and drawers. Pieces of cloth began to fly about the tiny room. The dressmaker draped and pinned a dark red fabric around Eleanor. Before the girl's surprised eyes, a dress began to take shape. The dressmaker stuck her with a pin, but Eleanor hardly felt it, she was so interested.

At last, the dressmaker clapped her hands together. She pushed Eleanor in front of a cracked mirror. "If you like it this way, I can begin work on it at once."

"Like it?" Eleanor cried out. "I love it!"

Eleanor's face was flushed, her eyes shining. "You look beautiful in it," Miss Samaia said.

"No, no, not beautiful," Eleanor said, even now unable to accept such a compliment. "Just happy."

"Ah," the dressmaker said, "you must learn that happiness makes one beautiful."

"Then," Eleanor said softly, "I am beautiful."

CHAPTER 10

The Terrible Secret

Aunt Pussie was coming to Allenswood! She and Eleanor would go back together to the United States as soon as the school closed for summer vacation. Aunt Pussie had been traveling in Europe and thought it would be nice if the two of them went home together.

How much fun it would be on the long ocean voyage back to New York. Eleanor could catch up on all the news from home and there would be someone to whom she could tell all the things she had seen and done this year.

From the moment they went aboard the big passenger ship in Southampton, England, Aunt Pussie made it quite clear that she was in no mood for conversation. She paid as little attention as possible to Eleanor. At first, it didn't matter that much. There was so much to see and do aboard the ship. But when day followed day and Aunt Pussie refused to go to the dining room to eat and stayed up most of each night sobbing, Eleanor decided she had to do something.

Finally, one afternoon, when Eleanor returned to their cabin after lunch and found her aunt in bed, her eyes red-rimmed, she felt she must learn what was wrong.

"Shall I go for the ship's doctor?" Eleanor asked.

"To treat a broken heart?"

Aunt Pussie began to weep again.

Eleanor stared at her aunt. "Oh you!" Her aunt waved her away. "What could you know about falling in love?" Eleanor's face turned red.

"I'm sorry," Aunt Pussie said, sitting up in bed. "I didn't mean it. I'm just so upset." She smoothed the bed covers. "Come here and sit down. Let me tell you about it."

Eleanor sat down on the edge of the bed. Aunt Pussie told her that she had fallen madly in love with a hand-some Englishman, and that, because she had to go back to the United States, she was sure she would never see him again. "It was love at first sight for both of us," Aunt Pussie sobbed.

How wonderful to have a man fall in love with you! Aunt Pussie was probably right. This would never happen to Eleanor.

Pussie flung the covers off the bed. "I know I will

drown myself if I can't see him again! I know I will."

"But maybe you will," Eleanor said. She put her hands on her aunt's forehead and began to stroke it, the way she used to do when her mother had a bad headache. "You will feel better when we get back to New York."

"You don't understand," her aunt sighed. "There's no point in my telling you any more."

Gently, Eleanor kept rubbing her aunt's forehead until, slowly, Aunt Pussie calmed down.

The long days at sea worked their magic. By the end of the ocean trip, Aunt Pussie seemed at ease and cheerful, herself again.

They had no sooner docked in New York, it seemed to Eleanor, than they were getting ready to travel again. It had been arranged for Eleanor and Aunt Pussie to spend the early part of the summer in Northeast Harbor, Maine, with cousin Susie Parish and her mother.

Aunt Pussie's good mood lasted just as long as the trip to Maine. It was a terribly hot day in Northeast Harbor, the kind that comes just before a violent summer storm. Aunt Pussie was short tempered and Eleanor did something that made her angry. Aunt Pussie stormed out of the house, slamming the door behind her. She sat down in a chair on the front porch.

Eleanor followed her out to say she was sorry.

"Oh, let me alone," Pussie snapped. "You ought to go inside and comb your hair. It looks awful."

"It's so hot today. That's why I put it up in a bun."

"I don't suppose it even matters to you how you look. Nobody's going to catch a man way off up here, anyway. When I think that in London—" Aunt Pussie broke off, her eyes filling with tears. "Oh, why did I have to remind myself . . . ?"

"If you are both in love with one another, why don't you marry him?" Eleanor asked, somewhat sharply.

"Because I found out right from the start that he was a drinking man."

Eleanor frowned. "But if you married him, wouldn't he change?"

"Change!" Pussie lashed out. "You must be out of your mind. Did your father ever change, after he started drinking?"

Eleanor stepped back. "My father—"

"Oh, come now, don't play the innocent girl with me. You must have known that's why your father was away so much."

"But he was sick," Eleanor protested.

"Yes—sick from drinking. It's all right. I know how you adored him. But I won't fool myself the way you do. Look at Vallie—my own brother."

"Uncle Vallie?"

"Your Uncle Vallie is practically a prisoner. Grandmother has her hands full trying to keep him hidden away."

"I know Vallie acts funny sometimes—"

"Acts funny?" Pussie laughed bitterly. "Drunk, you

mean. I won't live the kind of life your mother suffered. Your father killed her with his drinking."

Eleanor clapped her hands over her ears. "No, no! Not my father! You are lying!"

Eleanor could find no peace now with the friends and family around her. There was only one place left for her, only one person in the whole world who might understand her broken heart. She must return to Miss Souvestre and Allenswood!

Grandmother Hall agreed that it might be best for Eleanor to go back to England. But she was told firmly that at the end of that school year she must return to New York to make her formal bow to society.

Eleanor sailed for England, leaving behind a family excited by most unexpected news. President William McKinley had been shot and killed. On September 14th, 1901, Eleanor's Uncle Ted, who had been elected Vice President with McKinley, would become President of the United States.

To Eleanor, it was hard to believe. Jolly, lively Uncle Ted the President!

Eleanor studied hard her last year at Allenswood. She felt completely at home now, with the teachers, with her school mates. Every possible free time she and Miss Souvestre went on a trip. At Christmas, they toured to Rome. And with each trip, the year came closer to an end. With summer, Eleanor's school days would be over.

Would she be ready for a life that was expected of

her? The next October, Eleanor would be 18 years old. She would have to "come out" and take her place in New York society. It was a natural and accepted part of life for the daughter in a wealthy and prominent family. It never occurred to Eleanor that she had any choice in the matter.

During the summer after her return from Allenswood, she stayed at her grandmother's summer house. There she saw for herself the trouble her Uncle Vallie caused with his drinking.

Because of him, very few people, other than close friends and relatives, were invited to the beautiful home on the Hudson River. One by one, the hot summer days dragged by. The house had become a prison for Eleanor as well as for Uncle Vallie. Aunt Pussie made the best of things by flitting from romance to romance. Eleanor's brother, Hall, escaped by burying himself in his studies.

Now it was September and there was no more time to waste. Plans must be made for Eleanor's coming out into society. Everything had to be arranged, down to the last invitation.

Grandmother Hall was spending almost all her time caring for Uncle Vallie and shielding him from the outside world. Already she had decided that she and he would not return to the city but would stay on at the summer house. Eleanor and Aunt Pussie would go to New York and live alone with the servants.

The family gathered round to help Eleanor. One aunt ordered her dresses from Paris. Cousin Susie Parish and her husband agreed to go with Eleanor to the parties she would have to attend. Aunt Pussie explained all that would be expected of her in making her formal bow to society.

Her family was doing everything possible to make the occasion a success. Now it was up to her.

Aunt Pussie became as excited as though she were coming out all over again. "You have no idea what it's like," she told Eleanor eagerly. "You will be invited to the most wonderful parties. It is going to be the most thrilling time of your life."

How wonderful it would be to feel so sure, to know that a party would be fun, that every dance would be taken. If only all these invitations were for Aunt Pussie. She would go off happily to each one, smiling with confidence.

Eleanor discovered what the year ahead had in store for her at her first Assembly Ball. It was a beautiful affair, limited to the most important names in New York society.

Eleanor couldn't hide her fear as she entered the glittering ball room. Cousin Susie Parish and her husband were with her. If they had not been on either side of her, Eleanor might have turned and fled. In all of that gay, whirling crowd, she knew only two men. One was Bob Ferguson, an old friend of the family. The other was Forbes Morgan, who was a friend of Aunt Pussie's and who had eyes for no one else.

Eleanor sat down stiffly, next to Mrs. Parish. The music began. Slowly, a few couples drifted out onto the floor. Soon the floor was filled. The orchestra struck up a waltz, then a lively dance.

Mr. Parish glanced at Eleanor out of the corner of his eye and smiled at her. Eleanor forced herself to smile back. Cousin Susie leaned forward and patted Eleanor's hand. The couples on the floor clapped as the orchestra stopped.

Eleanor felt her hands grow damp inside her long white gloves. How much more of this could she endure? How long could she sit silent without bursting into tears?

Bob Ferguson came to Eleanor's rescue. He asked her to dance with him, then introduced her to several of his friends. Eleanor felt stiff and clumsy. After one dance with her, each of the boys seemed to feel that he had done his duty. They excused themselves and did not ask Eleanor to dance again.

The Assembly Ball was only the beginning of the social whirl in which Eleanor found herself trapped. Parties, dances, luncheons, teas, dinners and theater parties rolled by, one after another.

The young Eleanor Roosevelt, who had come to believe in herself as a free, independent person at Allenswood, was lost in this world that was supposed to be her own.

CHAPTER 11

Eleanor Has a "Feller"

By chance, a ray of sunshine broke through the dull round of Eleanor's social duties. One afternoon, on a train trip to visit her grandmother, Eleanor looked up and found her cousin Franklin standing next to her. She hadn't seen him since she was 14.

Franklin and his mother were on their way to their country home at Hyde Park. They were traveling in the Pullman, the more comfortable—and expensive—part of the train. Eleanor was seated in one of the coaches.

Franklin had been walking through the train to stretch his legs. He saw Eleanor, stopped to say "hello," and invited her to meet his mother.

At first, Eleanor hesitated. She had heard a great deal about the wealthy, famous Sara Delano Roosevelt. Most of what Eleanor had heard made her fear meeting Franklin's mother. She was, by reputation, a proud, sharp spoken woman.

Eleanor and Franklin were cousins by a common ancestor, Klaes Martensen van Roosevelt, who came to America from Holland in 1644. Two main branches of the Roosevelt family had become established in America. One family line finally led to Eleanor and her family, the other family line to Franklin and his family.

"Come along—please do! My mother won't eat you," Franklin said, smiling at Eleanor.

She glanced up at the handsome young man. His smile was as charming as her father's had been.

She stood up. Franklin took her arm to steady her in the moving train, and they walked through to the Pullman section.

Franklin quickly filled Eleanor in on some of the recent events in his life. He was now a student at Harvard. He had wanted to join the Navy, he said, but his father and mother had refused to give him permission. They both wanted him to stay closer to home. So he had given in and enrolled at Harvard, as they wished.

Just before they reached Mrs. Roosevelt's seat, Franklin told her that his father had died the year before.

Mrs. Roosevelt greeted Eleanor warmly. She turned out to be not half as frightening as Eleanor had expected. Indeed, she seemed very pleasant.

Sara Roosevelt talked about Eleanor's father. She and

her husband had met Elliott Roosevelt on an ocean voyage many years before. They had liked the charming young man so much that when Franklin was born, they had asked him to be the boy's godfather.

The train was getting close to Eleanor's stop. She stood up and excused herself. Franklin walked her back to her seat. "Mother is giving a party for some of my cousins in a few weeks," he told her, before saying good-by. "Don't be surprised if you receive an invitation."

Eleanor found herself smiling back easily. "Don't be surprised if I accept!"

Eleanor was invited to the house party at Hyde Park, accepted, and had a wonderful time with Franklin and his young cousins. After that, during the fall and winter season, Franklin came down from Cambridge to attend some of the dances in New York City.

Eleanor found that she and her cousin had many common interests. They both liked to read, and enjoyed many of the same authors. They both were interested in history. They had both been to Europe, and had explored many of the same places. Eleanor found she could exchange ideas and opinions with Franklin more easily than with other boys.

Then Franklin would return to Harvard University, and Eleanor would again find herself caught up in the whirl of dances and parties—and hating it.

Finally, there came the time when she could no longer bear her life in society. She began to look for something more important to occupy her time.

The Junior League was in the process of being formed. It was a new organization of young women from some of the outstanding families in New York. They gathered together to work without pay in hospitals, settlement houses and other charity institutions.

Eleanor and Jean Reid, daughter of Whitelaw Reid, editor of the New York *Herald Tribune* newspaper, were asked to teach girls in the Rivington Street Settlement House. Jean was to play the piano and Eleanor was to lead the girls in exercises and—of all things—dancing.

The Rivington Street Settlement House was in a slum area on New York's Lower East Side. Jean Reid usually came to her classes in a beautiful carriage. Eleanor often took the horse-drawn street car to a stop several blocks away. It gave her a chance to walk through the neighborhood where her little girls lived.

Eleanor was shocked by the conditions she saw. Garbage reeked in the long, dark halls of the old houses. Piles of refuse clogged the gutters. Often, young boys, dressed in rags, were fast asleep on the sidewalk.

The smell of stale beer came from the many bars. Pigs could be heard grunting in the depths of cellars, where they were kept. Peddlers hawked their pots and pans and household goods through streets filled with people. Over-ripe fruits and old vegetables were on sale, at

bargain prices, on wooden pushcarts at street corners.

New York's Lower East Side was jammed with families who had come from all parts of Europe to seek a better way of life in America. What they had found was dirt and poverty.

"There must be something I can do to help these people," Eleanor thought as she mounted the steps of the settlement house.

Jean was worried about these walks that Eleanor took in the slum neighborhood. One day, when it began to rain, Jean insisted that Eleanor go home with her in her carriage. "It's much too dangerous for you to walk these streets alone," Jean said. "Most of the people would do you no harm, but there are a lot of bars, and men who have been drinking—"

"I'm not afraid of men who have been drinking," Eleanor said. "I know all about them."

"There's no telling what might happen to you," Jean insisted.

"I don't have anything to worry about," Eleanor said calmly. "Men don't pay attention to me."

But one man was paying attention to Eleanor. Franklin Delano Roosevelt was curious about Eleanor's work at the settlement house. He asked if he might stop in at her class the next time he was in New York. Eleanor agreed.

One afternoon, when the dancing class was almost

over, a sharp-eyed child spied someone looking in through the small glass pane in the door. "There's a man outside!" she cried.

Jean turned from the piano to quiet the children. "Eleanor, it's your cousin Franklin!" she exclaimed. She motioned to him to come in.

The tall, handsome young man entered slowly. "I hope I'm not disturbing you," Franklin said. "I stopped by to take Eleanor home."

"No, we are just finishing up for the day," Jean said, gathering her things together.

"I will see you to your carriage," Franklin said to Jean. He turned to Eleanor with a bright smile. "Perhaps we can have dinner together this evening."

The children crowded around Eleanor while Franklin was gone.

"Is he your feller?" one of the little girls asked.

"My feller?" Eleanor looked at her blankly. "What do you mean?" Then she understood, and her pale face flushed at the thought.

"Of course not," she said quickly—much too quickly. "He's my cousin—a distant cousin—a fifth cousin, once removed—" This sent the children off into squeals of laughter.

"But he's your feller, isn't he?" the little girl kept on.

No, Eleanor had to admit to herself, he wasn't. Franklin had been kind to her this past winter, calling at the house, serving as her partner at dances. But he was an only son, and spoiled by a loving mother. Besides, he had not yet graduated from college.

"My feller," she thought. No, at best, Franklin was a friend.

Eleanor's days now were filled with all kinds of odds and ends, and she didn't really fit into a pattern anywhere.

Her empty life upset her more and more. Her work with the Junior League was not enough to keep her busy. She heard about another new organization, the Consumers' League, which was fighting to improve the conditions of workers in factories and stores. Eleanor decided to find out more about it.

One day she went along with a member who was inspecting some dress factories in downtown New York. As they waited for a street car, the woman handed Eleanor a booklet which described working conditions in places that were so bad they were called "sweat shops."

The sweat shop was an evil brought about by the factory system. During the 1800s, factories made it possible for the first time to turn out clothing of all kinds rapidly and cheaply. All that was needed was an equally cheap supply of labor.

Immigrants had begun streaming into the United States. They were driven to accept any jobs, at any wages, to keep alive. Many of the immigrants were skilled tailors. They took jobs in the skirt, dress and clothing factories that crowded one another in lower New York.

Men, women and children earned a bare living by the sweat of their brows in these "sweat shops." The women had to work so close together they sometimes rubbed elbows. Men received five dollars a week for working 80 hours.

Women, skilled in making lace, labored long hours at night to add to their husbands' small wages. Parents even sent young children into the factories to add a few pennies to the family's income.

By the time the street car arrived that morning, Eleanor had read enough in the booklet to set her hands trembling. She could hardly believe that the conditions described were possible.

As the two women seated themselves on a wooden bench in the street car, Eleanor opened the booklet again. She saw the printed words:

One and three-quarters million children between the ages of 10 and 15 were employed as of 1900.

"I can't believe it," Eleanor said.

The woman from the Consumers' League shook her head sadly.

"Miss Roosevelt, I want you to remember those are not just figures—they are *children*."

They got off the horse-drawn street car and walked

several blocks. As they entered a wooden loft building, the woman turned to Eleanor. "Take a deep breath, Miss Roosevelt," she said. "You won't have any more fresh air until we get out."

At the top of a long flight of wooden stairs, Eleanor stepped into one of the sweat shops she had just been reading about. She could not believe her eyes. She almost tumbled over a girl of about ten, with a thin face and half closed eyes. The little girl kept picking up the pieces of scrap material from the floor as they fell off the tables.

There was one window in the large loft. It faced a dirty brick building that shut out nearly all light. About 100 women bent over whirring machines in the thick, dead air. After 15 minutes, Eleanor could take no more. She stumbled down the stairs, shocked and shaken.

After this glimpse into the lives of some of New York's working class, Eleanor could not go back to playing the role of young society girl. There was so much misery in the world! How could she blind herself to it?

But few of her friends were interested. She needed someone to talk to who would understand. She looked forward to Franklin's visits to New York. He, at least, understood what she was talking about. But he was very busy at college, and could not come to New York very often.

Some of Eleanor's time was taken up with her brother Hall. He had always been taught at home by private teachers, but now Grandmother had decided that he should go to Groton, the same boarding school that Franklin had attended in Massachusetts.

Eleanor went along when her grandmother took Hall to the school to enroll him.

On the train ride, she sat next to her brother, talking cheerfully.

"You are going to like it at boarding school," Eleanor assured Hall. "I can come up to see you whenever you are allowed to have visitors."

"I'm glad to get a chance to study with other boys. Anyway, it was getting rough with Uncle Vallie at home," Hall admitted. He looked quickly across at his grandmother, who was sitting with her eyes closed. "I'm going to do my best, Eleanor. Don't worry about me. I'll be fine."

As she left her brother at Groton, Eleanor felt a small comfort. Harvard was not very far away. If Hall needed someone to turn to in a hurry, he could call on their cousin Franklin.

When the time came for the first visiting parents' day at Groton, Grandmother Hall felt she could not leave Vallie. Eleanor understood her grandmother's difficult position—but she also knew it would be dreadful if her brother did not have any visitors at all. So it was Eleanor who went, not only that first time, but all during the six years that Hall attended Groton. It was a pleasant trip and she liked seeing her brother.

Eleanor visited her brother on all the special parents' days. She called upon the head master, Reverend Peabody, whenever she went to Groton, to see how Hall was doing in his studies. She spoke to Hall's teachers to find out if he needed help. She read his English themes. She checked over his history reports. She lectured him about keeping neat, and she brought him little gifts. She was both father and mother to him and they enjoyed each other's company.

Eleanor had no idea, when she set out to see Hall one visiting day, that it was to be a very important day in her own life.

She was staying at Mrs. Whitney's boarding house at

Groton. She had come with a maid, as Grandmother Hall would not allow her to travel anywhere alone. Many other visitors were staying at the boarding house. There was a good deal of noise and coming and going of parents and students.

On the afternoon of the first day, Mrs. Whitney knocked on her door and called, "There is a young man to see you." Going downstairs, Eleanor found her cousin Franklin in the front hall.

She was surprised to see that Franklin was very nervous. She invited him into the parlor, where guests were allowed to entertain, for a cup of tea. Eleanor's maid trailed after them. She sat down quietly in a corner and began to turn the pages of an old issue of *Harper's Weekly*.

Franklin started to drink the tea, which Eleanor had poured. Suddenly, he put the tea cup down so quickly it rattled in the plate. "Eleanor, I love you," he burst out. "And—and—" He gazed around at the passing people. His eyes moved to the silent maid in the corner. "There just isn't any place where I can talk to you alone! But I didn't want to wait any longer."

The words rang in Eleanor's ears. Had she actually heard Franklin say *I love you?* She was too surprised to think about what the words really meant.

"Will it be all right if I tell Mother right away?"

Eleanor caught her breath. Would Sara Delano Roosevelt give her son permission to marry? Mrs. Roosevelt adored her son and kept him close to her side.

Finally, Eleanor found her voice. "What will your mother say?"

Franklin stood up. "Eleanor," he said firmly, "I love you. Remember that. Will you marry me?"

She looked into his blue eyes. "Yes, Franklin."

CHAPTER 12

Happy Memories

As Eleanor had feared, Sara Delano Roosevelt wanted Franklin to think it over.

Mrs. Roosevelt offered all kinds of reasons. They were both too young. Neither was ready for marriage. Eleanor, at 19, knew nothing of the demands of marriage. Franklin, at 21, had not as yet decided upon a career. Wait, Mrs. Roosevelt urged. Don't make any formal announcement of the engagement yet.

Franklin, the loving son, gave in. Eleanor, obedient to the wishes of those older than she, agreed.

But the distress in Eleanor's heart would not yield to any arguments. She could no longer hide the love she had for Franklin. It all came pouring out in a simple letter that she sent to Sara Roosevelt.

Eleanor's hand trembled as she wrote: "I know how you feel and how hard it must be." She started to cross out the line. Eleanor wondered what she could say to make Sara Roosevelt understand that she, in her way, loved Franklin as much as Mrs. Roosevelt did. Slowly, her pen moved on. "I do so want you to learn to love me a little. I will always try to do what you wish, for I have grown to love you."

Eleanor folded and sealed the letter. There was nothing more she could do—but wait.

February of 1904 was cold and dismal in New York. Eleanor felt out of sorts and blamed it on the weather. She made a great effort to cheer herself up. Her Aunt Pussie was being married on February 16th to Forbes Morgan, who adored her. Eleanor did her best to help her Aunt Pussie. She eagerly ran last-minute errands that needed to be attended to, as she had when she was a child.

And then came chilling news. Sara Delano Roosevelt was taking Franklin off on a trip. He and Lathrop Brown, his room mate at Harvard, were to spend six weeks in the West Indies. Mrs. Roosevelt's excuse was that Franklin had been studying very hard and needed a rest.

Eleanor had no one to turn to for comfort. Grandmother Hall had given up the house on West 37th Street. It was an expense she could no longer bear now that she had to keep the house at Tivoli open all year. Eleanor was staying with her cousin Susie Parish.

She felt shy about inviting guests to the Parish house. She did not want to cause her cousin any extra trouble. Eleanor felt lost and lonely. Pussie was married. Franklin was away on his trip. There didn't seem to be anyone around to whom Eleanor could talk freely. Eleanor didn't want to burden cousin Susie with her own problems.

Aunt Bye came to Eleanor's rescue, at just the right moment. She invited Eleanor to come to Washington to spend some time with her and her husband, Admiral William Sheffield Cowles.

Eleanor accepted the invitation eagerly. Aunt Bye's house, at 1733 N Street, was the center of lively activity. Uncle Ted—President Theodore Roosevelt—often dropped in, and the newspapers sometimes called it "The Little White House."

When Uncle Ted hurried in at odd moments for a brief chat with Aunt Bye, whose opinions he respected, Eleanor would sit quietly in a corner and listen while her uncle discussed some of the problems of running the government. What a fearful burden it was to be President!

She listened wide-eyed, beginning to understand the great range of decisions that fell to her uncle. He spoke of his concerns about big business. He mentioned his distress over the war which had broken out between Russia and Japan. It all seemed far away to Eleanor, but Theodore Roosevelt hoped to be able to bring the two countries together in peace in some way. It seemed to

Eleanor that her uncle spoke about these national and international affairs as if they were personal problems, close to his heart, that he had to solve himself.

At times, Aunt Bye would quietly interrupt. The President would pause and listen carefully to what his sister had to say.

It was a strange world to Eleanor—and her heart and mind were far away. As the weeks dragged by, she wondered if she had dreamed that Franklin had asked her to marry him.

She threw herself into the round of social affairs that her Aunt Bye arranged—teas, formal dinner parties, dances. She met many young and important government officials. She went visiting and to the shops with her aunt.

Alice Roosevelt came in one afternoon to see Eleanor and her Aunt Bye. She invited Eleanor to spend the night at the White House. "Sleep in the White House?" Eleanor laughed. "The idea is just too frightening. No thanks, Alice."

One evening, Aunt Bye stopped Eleanor before she went to bed. "I don't want to pry," her aunt began, "but I can see that something is troubling you. Are you upset about anything?"

"I'm fine, really I am," Eleanor said quickly. "It's just —it's—"

Aunt Bye looked at Eleanor's pale face. "If I didn't know better, I'd say you were in love." Aunt Bye broke off as she noticed Eleanor draw in her breath. Aunt Bye took Eleanor's hand. They walked silently into the drawing room. "Sit down, Eleanor. I see I've struck a soft spot."

Slowly, Eleanor sat down at her aunt's side. "I *am* in love," Eleanor admitted.

"With Franklin?" she guessed.

Eleanor nodded. "But it won't do me any good," she cried out. She could not disguise any more how miserable she felt. "His mother has taken him off on a trip."

"Eleanor," her aunt said seriously, "are you in love with Franklin—truly in love?"

"Oh, yes, Aunt Bye."

"Then your love will make him come back to you. Nothing can keep you apart."

Fate was on Eleanor's side this time. Sara Roosevelt and Franklin stopped in Washington at the end of their trip. Mrs. Roosevelt hoped she might be able to pull strings, to get a job abroad for Franklin.

Eleanor was surprised one afternoon to have a servant announce that Franklin Roosevelt was waiting in the drawing room for her. Hope mixed with fear as she hurried down to meet Franklin.

Eleanor had her answer the minute she entered the drawing room. Franklin spun around on hearing her steps. "Eleanor," he cried out. "How I've missed you!"

Sara Delano Roosevelt could not deny her son any longer. She had hoped for marriage for Franklin when he was older and settled in business. But, on December 1, 1904, the engagement of Franklin Delano Roosevelt and Eleanor Roosevelt was announced.

Franklin's love gave new meaning to Eleanor's life. So many thrilling things began to happen! In June of 1904, she was invited to be a guest at Franklin's graduation from Harvard. Sara Roosevelt was beginning to include Eleanor in the family circle.

During the early summer, Mrs. Roosevelt invited Eleanor to her home at Hyde Park. Eleanor grew to love the large country home near the Hudson River, where Franklin had been born and had lived most of his life. Its quiet charm reminded her a little of her Grandmother Hall's house.

Eleanor also spent a few days with the Roosevelts at their summer home on the small Canadian island of Campobello. If any doubt lingered in Eleanor's mind that Franklin loved her, the happy hours they spent together at Campobello put an end to it. Each day with Franklin was a link in a chain of happy memories for her.

But there was even greater excitement ahead. Uncle Ted had been elected for a second term and Aunt Bye invited Eleanor and Franklin to come to Washington to attend the ceremony, on March 4th, 1905, when Theodore Roosevelt would again take the oath as President of the United States.

Eleanor was fearful about going to Washington for this

great occasion. "I feel so stupid," she confessed to Franklin, as they boarded a special train to Washington. "I know so little about politics."

"It's an interesting field," Franklin said. "I'd like to get into it myself."

"But you've just started your law courses at Columbia—" Eleanor was too surprised to finish.

After graduating from Harvard, Franklin had registered for law school at Columbia University in New York City.

She was surprised at the idea that Franklin might be interested in politics. She knew her Grandmother Hall would not approve. She was certain Franklin's mother would feel the same way. And what about herself? Could she be happy if Franklin made up his mind to throw himself into the public spot light?

Now she heard Franklin saying, "Studying law can be a grind, but I'm going to stick it through."

"Law isn't only in books," Eleanor said. "Law is in people—in helping people."

The streets of Washington were jammed. People had been lining up since early morning for the parade. Young children, carried on the shoulders of their parents, waved little flags. Stores were decked out in banners, and flags were draped across many of the government buildings.

Eleanor tingled with excitement. She and Franklin hurried to Aunt Bye's. A carriage was waiting to take them to the Capitol building, where Theodore Roosevelt

would make his address. Eleanor and Franklin were shown to seats reserved for honored guests, close to the President and his immediate family.

Cousin Alice caught Eleanor's eyes. She raised her hand and waved.

"My goodness, she's smiling," Eleanor gasped. "How can she look so calm? I feel frightened just sitting here."

"To tell the truth, I'm nervous, too," Franklin said.

Eleanor laughed. "I don't think we will ever see another President of the United States in our family!"

The beat of drums sounded from the distance. A military guard took its place on the steps of the Capitol building. The men were smart in their uniforms, their brass buttons catching the sun. A stir of excitement rippled through the crowd.

A great cheer rose from the crowd when her Uncle Ted went to the front of the platform to begin his speech. Theodore Roosevelt's voice rang out clear and sharp as a bugle in the cool spring air. Afterward, when Franklin and she went to a luncheon at the White House, Eleanor admitted she had been so caught up in the excitement she could not recall one single word of her uncle's address.

Later in the afternoon, she and Franklin watched the grand parade. Down a side street into Pennsylvania Avenue came a unit of soldiers, mounted on sleek horses. The banners of their regiment were lifted high and swelled like sails in the sharp spring wind.

"Hurray for the Rough Riders," a little boy shouted, and another caught it up, "Hurray for Teddy, the hero of San Juan Hill."

Franklin grinned, turning to Eleanor. "Hurray for Uncle Teddy, who is coming to our wedding!"

Theodore Roosevelt had agreed to give his niece away in marriage. As President, he had a full schedule. The wedding would have to be held at a time to suit him.

Even so important a time as her wedding date, Eleanor allowed others to choose for her. Various dates were suggested. Finally, it was decided that Eleanor and Franklin would be married on March 17th, 1905.

Theodore Roosevelt was coming to New York for the St. Patrick's Day parade. He would sandwich Eleanor's wedding in between two speeches he had to make that day. Eleanor quickly agreed to the date, because March 17th had been her mother's birthday.

Besides, she was thankful to have a date set—any date. It made the coming marriage a little more real, a little less like a lovely dream that might vanish.

CHAPTER 13

"Till Death Us Do Part"

Eleanor stood in front of a full-length mirror in Mrs. Ludlow's bedroom. Nervously she straightened the lace veil that fell over her long-sleeved satin wedding gown. A diamond half-moon pin, which had belonged to her mother, glittered in her hair.

All the wedding arrangements had been made by Eleanor's cousin Susie and her mother, who lived in houses next to each other on East 66th Street. Both houses were to be used for the wedding ceremony and for receiving the guests later. A common sliding door between them had been thrown open to take care of the huge crowd of guests expected for the wedding.

Reverend Endicott Peabody, head master at Groton, had agreed to perform the wedding ceremony. It was to be held before an altar set up in front of the fireplace in Mrs. Ludlow's drawing room. Food was to be served in the library of Mrs. Parish's house. Fancy dishes were already spread out on long tables that had been set up there.

Now there was nothing for Eleanor to do but wait. Her attendants fluttered about her. They were all looking for her Uncle Ted. He had promised to come as soon as he could after making his speech at the St. Patrick's Day parade.

Cousin Alice Roosevelt, her maid of honor, came into the room where Eleanor waited. She was dressed in a silk gown, with three plumes in her hair. Laughing, she chased out the chattering girls.

"I want a word with my cousin," Alice said. As the door closed behind the girls, Alice explained, "I thought you would like a quiet moment." She stood in front of Eleanor, gazing at her. "You look as if you had come straight out of Tiffany's window," Alice said. "You are all a-glitter."

Eleanor wore a wide necklace of pearls which Franklin's mother had given her. On her dress sparkled a diamond bow knot, a gift from Franklin's aunt, Mrs. Warren Delano.

Alice bent down and sniffed the bouquet of lilies-of-the-valley lying on a table. "Now, be sure to look where I'm standing when you throw your bouquet!" Alice pleaded with a laugh.

A shout went up outside the house. Alice looked out the window. "Just as I thought, it's Papa. How is he ever going to get through that crowd? Eleanor, do you know—there are people jammed solid from the street to the very doorway!"

In a little while, President Theodore Roosevelt came rushing into the bedroom. "Well, well, let's see the bride." He brushed off his wrinkled coat sleeves. "I must say, I thought I would smother in that crush."

People packed the streets outside, hoping to see the President and the famous guests who had been invited to the wedding. The crowds were so thick in front of the Parish house that many of the invited guests could not get through to see the wedding ceremony.

It was time. Eleanor was coming down the stairs, on the arm of her Uncle Theodore. Her heavy satin wedding train flowed down the steps behind her, and across the floor, as she moved slowly toward the altar. It was decorated with vases of flowers, and the heavy perfume floated out to meet Eleanor as she moved forward.

The room was filled with people. Only a small space had been cleared for the wedding party to walk through.

Eleanor saw Reverend Peabody standing before the altar. He had his head bowed over the white satin Bible he held before him.

Eleanor's eyes dimmed. She had not been able to pick out Franklin and his best man, Lathrop Brown.

Suddenly Eleanor did see her brother Hall, in the line

of attendants marching in. Her throat was tight. The familiar strains of the "Wedding March" floated across the softly murmuring throng. Eleanor took another few steps forward.

Uncle Ted gave her hand a squeeze before he released her. "You are doing fine," she heard him whisper. "I told you, you are a true Roosevelt."

Another few steps forward and Eleanor was at Franklin's side. She lifted her head and stood proud and tall. The simple ceremony went forward until at last Franklin slipped the wedding band on her finger. The words of the service rang in Eleanor's ears: "Till death us do part . . ." And it was over.

Eleanor scarcely noticed that her Uncle Ted had turned from her side and was heading for the library. As if he were the Pied Piper, the guests began streaming after the President. Eleanor found herself standing alone for a moment, separated even from Franklin by the pressing crowd of guests. A chill went through her. On the greatest day of her life, she was once again alone, alone in a sea of people. Her throat grew tight and dry, as it had so many times in the past. She turned to flee, and tripped over the train on her wedding gown. And then Franklin pushed through to her and put out his hand to steady her—and she knew that from then on, she need never be afraid again.

CHAPTER 14

First Lady of the World

There were to be many trying times for Eleanor and Franklin Delano Roosevelt over the years. There was to be the terrible summer of 1921 when Franklin came down with polio and was left crippled. Later on, there would be Franklin's return to politics, spurred on by Eleanor. Slowly, the Roosevelts would climb up the political ladder from the Governor's house in Albany, New York, to the White House in Washington, D.C., in 1932.

Still later, there would be more lonely scenes. Franklin's death on April 12th, 1945, marked the end of one life for Eleanor, the beginning of another. She was called upon to represent her country at the United Nations. Here she fought to have the Universal Declaration of

Human Rights accepted. It was an inspiring statement of the rights of all men everywhere. It was to be one of the great triumphs of the United Nations and of Eleanor's career.

But on March 17th, 1905, standing happy and glowing at her husband's side, Eleanor could not know what was ahead. There had always been a deep well of hidden strength in Eleanor. As she started her married life, she began to tap these resources.

Eleanor felt it was a wife's duty to be interested in whatever interested her husband. When Franklin's interests turned to politics, she became a part of his political life.

Marriage also brought new joy for Eleanor. On May 3rd, 1906, Anna Eleanor—the first and only daughter they were to have—was born to Eleanor and Franklin Roosevelt. As the years passed, four lively sons were added to the family.

Eleanor Roosevelt could have lived in a small comfortable world of her own. But she chose to embrace the wide world of her fellow man.

She was surrounded by wealth, but she learned what it meant to be poor. She was very much aware of suffering, of the smallest hurts, of unkind acts to others.

She learned early to help others. She asked for no thanks, no praise. She did the right thing simply because that was what she wanted most to do.

Franklin Delano Roosevelt became President during one of the worst depressions in our nation's history. Millions were out of work. Many businesses had had to shut down.

"The only thing we have to fear is fear itself," Franklin Delano Roosevelt called out at his first speech, when he took office. But his stirring words had to be put into action. Eleanor Roosevelt became his eyes and ears in those places where he could not go himself. She investigated factories and coal mines. She flew to Europe and the South Pacific. She was able to find out what the people of the nation thought. She did this with sympathy and understanding.

Eleanor Roosevelt had in her the promise of being a great woman, and that promise had been fulfilled.

In time, the little girl who had been afraid to say a few simple words, even in the school room in her own house, lectured to thousands.

In time, the shy child who had felt that her ideas were of no worth, grew up to write books, newspaper and magazine columns, without fear of expressing her frank opinions.

In time, the lonely 18-year-old, afraid of New York society, grew into a woman who entertained world leaders at the White House.

In time, the clumsy child who was such a disappointment grew into a beautiful woman. Each deed—each act of kindness—left its mark on Eleanor Roosevelt's face.

It was the face of a good woman—and so, a beautiful woman . . .

Eleanor Roosevelt grew up surrounded with doubts and fears about herself, and became without fear in her battles for others. For many more years than any other President's wife, Eleanor Roosevelt was First Lady of the United States.

On her death, November 7th, 1962, she was called First Lady of the World.